FOUL HORDES

THE PICTS
IN THE
NORTH EAST
AND THEIR
BACKGROUND

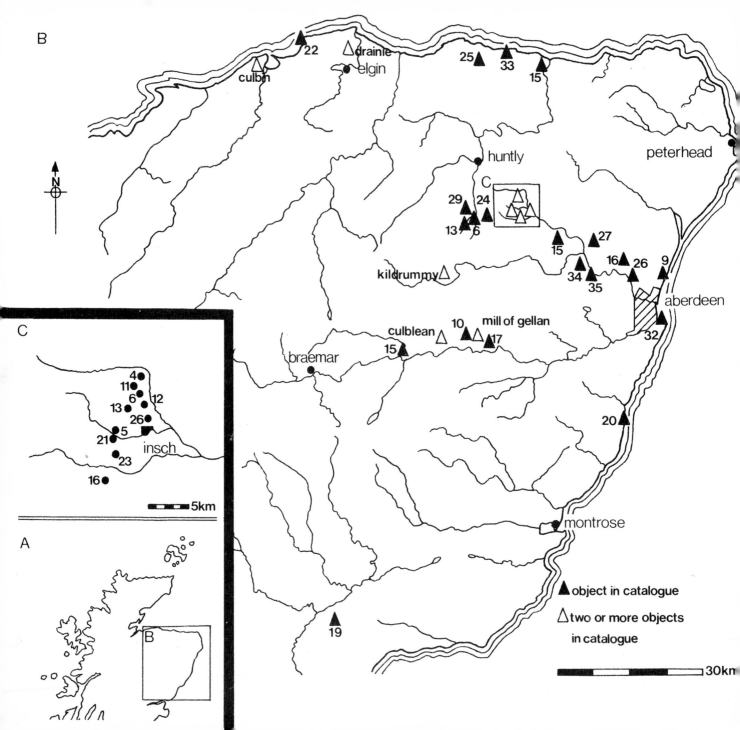

Foul Hordes:
the Picts in the North-East and their background

IAN RALSTON & JIM INGLIS

AE2
10.
9800142

ISBN A367

Printed by Waverley Press (Aberdeen) Limited

ACKNOWLEDGEMENTS

We wish to thank the following for their financial support of the exhibition:

British Airways
Grampian Television PLC
Marathon Oil UK Ltd
Shell UK Exploration & Production

The following institutions kindly lent objects in their care:

British Museum
Moray District Council Museums Service
Moray Society (Elgin Museum)
National Museum of Antiquities of Scotland
National Trust for Scotland
North East Libraries Museums Service

Many individuals provided material for display or assistance of various kinds.
We extend our thanks to:

Mr P Ashmore, Mr T Cowie, Dr H Fairhurst, Ms L Gray
Hodder & Stoughton Childrens Books
Dr L R Laing, Mr J Livingston, Mr G MacDonald, Mr I Morrison
Mr D Rathbone, Dr A Ritchie, Dr J N G Ritchie, Mr I A G Shepherd
Dr N Trewin, Dr T F Watkins, Mr W G Watt, Dr G Whittington
Dr A A Woodham

All aerial photographs were taken by Aberdeen Archaeological Surveys
Crown Copyright Reserved

Cover Design:
Gordon Robertson, DA

Photograph of Burghead Bull (Cat No 22) by
Mr I Morrison
Moray District Council Museums

DATE	EVENT	PICTISH SCULPTURE CLASS		
		1	2	3
AD 84	Battle of Mons Graupius			
297	Eumenius makes first mention to Picts			
450	Picts and Scots devastate North Britain			
540	Gildas writes his 'De Excidio Britonum'			
565	Columba visits Bridei King of northern Picts			
658	Oswiu of Northumbria annexes part of South Pictland			
664	Synod of Whitby			
20 V 685	Battle of Nechtansmere			
697	Adamnan writes his 'Vita Sancti Columbae'			
731	Bede writes his 'Historia Ecclesiastica Gentis Anglorum'			
741	Picts under Oengus mac Fergus subdue Dalriada			
843	Kenneth mac Alpin King of Picts and Scots			
934	Aethelstan of England 'wastes' Scotland to Dunnottar			
1057	Macbeth slain at Lumphanan			

Introduction

For many years, the term 'Pictish' has been synonymous with all that is idiosyncratic in the archaeology of northern Scotland in the centuries after the beginning of our era. Pictish studies have been viewed as a series of interlocking problems, each of which adds a dimension to the separateness of cultural traditions north of the Forth-Clyde isthmus and emphasises differences with the Celtic, Roman, British or Anglian peoples who came into contact with the Picts or their precursors. However, in recent decades, more stress has been laid on Pictish participation in wider developments in Dark Age Britain, and we hope that this exhibition may do something to diminish the apparent remoteness of things Pictish from the mainstream of early British societies, whilst not suggesting that recognisable distinctions are absent. The exhibition concentrates on the archaelogical remains from the North-East Scottish mainland, in the core area of Pictland, but paradoxically less well researched than either the Northern Isles, for example, or Angus and neighbouring counties further south.

It is perhaps appropriate to begin by defining the nature of the evidence. The early centuries AD in Scotland may be characterised as a protohistoric period, for which a certain amount of historical information is available to us. Here 'history' is taken to encompass written sources, for the most part in Latin, and including both material composed in the British Isles and further afield. Comparatively little of this evidence is likely to have been committed to the page in Pictish-controlled areas. Almost all, in the form in which it has survived, is at no less than one remove from North-East Scotland in the early centuries AD, either in space or in time, and frequently both. Sources to which we will make reference were produced as far afield as Alexandria in Egypt, and, in some cases, closer in time to ourselves than to the events they purport to document. For example, any source on Saint Columba written after the late 13th century is further removed from the foundation of Iona than from 1984.

A second strand of evidence is provided by names of places, both man-made and natural. On skilled analysis, these can provide evidence of the language spoken by the original name-giver. Another correlation between language and place is offered by inscriptions carved on objects, particularly those which are difficult to transport and therefore likely to have been produced on-site, or at least nearby. For these, the form of alphabet used may also be instructive. The third principal set of material is archaeological, and includes both sites and monuments as well as objects. It goes without saying that none of this material is stamped 'Made by a Pict in Pictland', and our inferences are thus largely conditioned by considerations of style, material, and distribution.

All three suites of evidence—linguistic, historical, archaelogical—have been subjected to attrition across the centuries. Amongst the problems which afflict historical domumentation, we may include the loss of documents, poor copying during the medieval period, later interpolations and additions, invention by the original author for literary effect or to mask ignorance, and the fact that some of the items used nowadays in discussions of this period were not intended as historical records in the first place, but were rather written to achieve other ends.

The archaeological evidence which has survived is a product of its own durability, and its subsequent recognition. This durability is a result of the materials used, whether in the construction of monuments or the production of objects. Recognition in more recent times has led to collection and study, but much remains to discover. Objects have suffered from natural processes of decay, both biological and chemical: the almost-complete absence of iron objects in the exhibition is symptomatic. Other kinds of loss affect the record in different ways, for example through coastal erosion undermining cliff-top settlements. Yet other sites have been lost across the centuries by subsequent human activities: these include ploughing, afforestation, road-building and the like, as well as much more calculated degradations, such as the spate of destruction of earlier religious monuments which followed the Reformation in some areas. Whilst much of the lowland area of the North-East, in common with other long-farmed areas, now shows few surface traces of previous human activity, air photography under suitable conditions can reveal sites of former settlements, burials and so on, through differences in crop growth. In sum, the archaeological record has been subjected to destructive forces and detective effort in varying degrees across the landscapes of the area which interests us.

The record of placenames offers a palimpsest of various of the languages which have been spoken in the North-East. The process of naming is a continuous one, and involves not only renaming, but also altering pre-existing names to suit new languages and modes of speech. Thus names are on occasion compositely built up, with elements derived from different languages. Depending on the degrees of differentiation and of substitution between one language and its successor, the level of replacement may vary from the very partial to the near-complete. Wherever possible, the earliest versions of names should therefore be used in assessing the linguistic make-up of our area in the Dark Ages. As with the archaelogical record, absence of evidence is not evidence of absence, but, in the linguistic sense, may simply reflect widespread replacement.

In conclusion, the very incompleteness of all three data sources means that there will never be a single view of what North-East Scotland was like one and a half millennia ago. Disputes continue over such basic features as chronology, especially in terms of the archaeological record, in which the period and duration of use of certain items remains unclear.

Rather than adhering to one school of thought in preference to another, we have tried to indicate chronological ranges for site and artefact types. Our problem is compounded by the comparative lack of excavations in the core area, since this archaeological activity offers a prime means of controlling some of our assertions.

Thirty years ago, in discussing the three kinds of evidence outlined above, Dr F T Wainwright remarked that '. . . no problem is at once so seductive and so treacherous as that of the Picts. So many reputations have been shattered that only the confident and the careless will today venture into this graveyard of rejected theories' (Wainwright, 1955, 13). Whilst we hope to have avoided undue carelessness in the presentation of the following material, changed days mean that we have every confidence that new information will allow the material discussed below to be reformulated into braver configurations as re-assessment takes place in the future.

Elsewhere in Scotland artificial islands called crannogs were still inhabited during the Dark Ages. This example near Cullen, is however, undated.

Iron Age background: northern tribes

There is nothing to suggest that the inhabitants of North-East Scotland labelled as Picts by their contemporaries and successors were other than the descendants of the native army which had stood so unsuccessfully against Agricola and his legions at the battle of Mons Graupius in 83 or 84 AD. Whilst strictly it is illogical for us to refer to 'Picts' before their first appearance in a classical text (this occurs late in the third century AD), there is no evidence to indicate substantial immigration to this portion of the country over the intervening years. Indeed, the term 'Pict' may have been coined as a Roman soldiers' epithet for the barbarians on the northern fringe who periodically raided southward. It may not, originally at least, have defined an identifiable people with a distinguishable culture.

The Iron Age forerunners of the Picts, sometimes called proto-Picts, thus first appear on the stage of history through classical references to them, gleaned as a result of the northward expansion of the Roman Empire. These sources can be complemented by the use of the archaeological record, which displays manifest regional differences during the centuries before the first reference to Picts in 297 AD, and indeed continues so to do thereafter. Before outlining the content of the archaelogical record, it is worth noting that the initial historically-recorded threat to the forerunners of the Picts came from the South. Contrastingly, their successors, many centuries later, were to succumb to Viking expansion in the North, and Scotic pressures from the West, each of which is also better recorded than the internal affairs of the Picts. Much of our historical evidence is thus external to the group on which we wish to focus.

The Iron Age background of the Picts of the North-East may be considered to relate more readily to

Craggy cliffs supplement the ramparts of the later prehistoric fort at Turin Hill near Forfar. Two circular features in the enclosed area are later fortifications known as duns.

traditions further South in Scotland than to the Atlantic West and the northern mainland of the country. A simple list of monument types, prevalent in the last-mentioned areas, but absent in the North-East, clearly displays this difference. Brochs and their enveloping settlements, wheelhouses, and, in any significant numbers, the diminutive heavily-fortified enclosures called duns, are not a feature of our area. This differential appears to continue into the succeeding centuries of the Pictish period. For example, the range of amoeba-like house types, characterised as 'cellular' and 'figure-of-eight' (Ritchie and Ritchie, 1981, 177), and recorded from pre-Viking contexts on the Long Island and on Orkney, has not been recognised in the admittedly less well prospected zone with which we are concerned.

However, these differences are by no means absolute, and certain monument categories are recorded in both areas. For example, the North-East knuckle shares a tradition of circular stone-walled houses (often termed 'hut-circles') with many other areas of Highland Scotland. In our area, these tend to survive, sometimes grouped into small settlements, above the present cultivation margin, on fairly gentle slopes which, for one reason or another, have escaped cultivation or afforestation. Ogston's study (1931) remains the regional classic, and demonstrates that this type of monument may be integrated into systems of field banks, composed of low rickles of stone, stone clearance heaps, indicative of non-intensive agriculture, and hollow ways, a token of the movement of livestock and perhaps of wheeled carts. One of the best-preserved of such sites, at New Kinord in the Howe of Cromar, may be taken to imply that such undefended farming settlements were once more extensively represented in the lowlands. Recent excavations, especially on Arran, coupled with the small quantities of remains recovered during the examination of some of the Culbean group in Cromar, suggest that such sites may have begun to be used late in the second millennuim BC, but the type appears to have continued until the end of the succeeding millennium. This is suggested by the radiocarbon dates

7

which indicate prolonged, if intermittent, occupation of the site of Kilphedir in Sutherland. Sites of this type in the North-East may have been the homes and work-places of farmers throughout the first millennium BC and into the early centuries of our era.

Recent work, especially in aerial survey, has suggested that timber-built roundhouses may have been of much greater significance during the later prehistory of the North-East than was previously realised. Most are known purely as cropmarks, but some, of varying type, may be detected by surface fieldwork. On the Hill of Dunnideer, near Insch, for example, a series of platforms, which would have made suitable stances for roundhouses on that steep-sided hill, is apparent. Whilst some of these have been enveloped by the outer defences of the composite fort which crowns the summit, others are excluded, suggesting that, in this instance at least, the platforms pre-date the external line of enclosure. Since this form of platform is essentially a response to slope conditions, it is by no means clear that all such platforms need necessarily pre-date the Pictish period.

Another form of house, better known south of the Mounth, and apparently belonging early in the

Circular and pennanular cropmarks in this field below the Hill of Newleslie, near Insch, probably represents the stances of wooden houses.

sequence, is distinguished by an internal penannular ditch. Such ring-ditch houses survive as upstanding

features to the south of the Feugh valley, as well as being suggested by the form of cropmark evidence elsewhere. Two sites in the Garioch display particular concentrations of these, one on the farm of Wester Fintray at Kintore, and a second below the Hill of Newleslie: in the Mearns, there appears to be a noteworthy group visible from the air at Pitten-gardner, near Fordoun. Other forms of timber-built round-houses are recorded, both in excavation on the promontory of Castle Point, Troup, at Dalladies, and by air photography at Gairloch, near Elgin, and elsewhere in the North-East. Whilst the likelihood is that the majority of these sites date from the first millennium BC, much of this chronology has to be imported from Southern Scotland, and need not hold true for our area.

A pointer in this direction comes from the examination of a site at Dalladies in the south of Kincardine. Here Watkins (1980a) investigated an enigmatic site which included both the post-rings of circular timber houses and a set of curvilinear ditches. This undefended settlement seems to have been occupied from the late pre-Roman Iron Age until about the 6th century AD. Few artefacts were recovered, but both iron-working and agriculture are attested, the latter represented by small quantities of animal bone, charred cereal grains and fragments of rotary querns. It is likely that this type of site continued to accommodate some of the Picts of succeeding generations, although we lack hard evidence from other places, like Burnhead of Monboddo north of Fordoun, a cropmark site which appears to display characteristics similar to Dalladies (Ralston, 1984, ill 4). The possibility that the Dalladies ditches—in which a variety of structural details were detected—served as places for the storage of both seed-crops and food, links them with the better-known architecture of the souterrains or earthhouses. Within Scotland, these curved, stone-walled, subterranean passages have been most frequently, although by no means exclusively, recognised in the area to the north of the Forth. Those south of the Mounth are by far the more thoroughly investigated (Wainwright, 1953;

1963; Barclay in Watkins, 1980b). Whilst it has long been known that some souterrains are associated with above-ground stone-built structures, Watkins' (1980b) examination of a site near Bankfoot in Perthshire demonstrated that such imposing underground galleries could also be related to circular timber buildings. The date range for these souterrains is situated conventionally in the first two centuries AD.

North of the Mounth, the major concentration of souterrains lies in upper Strathdon and in the Howe of Cromar. In contrast to Strathmore, where further examples of this type of site continue to be recognised in aerial photography, this activity has so far little altered the distribution in our area, and souterrains continue to be remarkable for their rarity in the coastal lowlands. Dating evidence, where available— essentially for work done in Edwardian times or earlier—and structural parallels, suggest that the main period of construction and use of souterrains lay in the proto-Pictish centuries. Rotary quern-stones, an innovation of considerable significance, are recorded from a number of North-East sites—at Buchaam in Strathdon, Culsh in Tarland, and the Muirs of Kildrummy—and match similar finds further South. Quern-stones were also found at the entrances of souterrains at Castle Newe in Strathdon and at Milton of Whitehouse, in the latter case at least apparently associated with a structure at ground level. Stone cups, probably cup-shaped lamps, (cf nos 1-6) were found in an example at Migvie.

For Aberdeenshire sites, the best dating evidence is provided by a Roman coin of 1st century AD date found with a pair of massive armlets (cf no 9) from the entrance of the souterrain discovered in the garden of Castle Newe. A rather less secure association exists between comparable armlets from Crossford, Coull, and enclosures and souterrains which were 'trenched' there in mid-Victorian times (Ogston, 1931, 79).

Elsewhere in the Howe of Cromar, Abercromby (1904) was able summarily to excavate, and Ogston (1931) to comment on, associations between 'hut-circles' and 'souterrains', demonstrating that the entrances to the latter lay within the former at Old, and possibly at New, Kinord. Whilst Ogston percipiently remarked on the possibility of the stone-built enclosures at Kinord having surrounded timber-built houses (1931, 16) the intimate and repeated association between above-ground structures and souterrains must surely negate the oft-repeated hypotheses that these structures served as 'bolt-holes' or as 'winter residences'. The eveness of the internal temperature of souterrains, coupled with the admittedly not strong evidence from their later contents, favours storage of perishables as a *raison d'etre*. If this is accepted, the volume of space in some of the larger souterrains suggests the former presence of farming communities with considerable surplus production to store.

Collectively, the varieties of structures discussed above suggest the widespread settlement of the region during the last millennium BC and in the proto-Pictish period. We are not in a position to offer secure terminal dates for their construction, and certain strands of evidence point, albeit very tentatively, to continued use of certain types of site, and, a little less insecurely, to repeated recourse to certain localities. The pins from Culbean, discussed below (no 28) may be taken as an example of the rather frustrating quality of some of the evidence presently available. But the radiocarbon dates from Newmill, at Bankfoot, and from Dalladies offer further intimations of continuity, although from further South.

In contrast to the rather tentative evidence for the continued use of undefended settlements, the record of the defended sites contains more, although hardly plentiful, indications of the repeated use of certain fortifications from the pre-Roman Iron Age into the first millennium AD. Certain of these sites will be discussed more fully below in relation to the Pictish evidence from them, and remarks here will be confined to a few general comments (Ralston, Sabine and Watt, 1983).

First, and most critically, there is nothing to suggest that these settlements were all contemporary. Details of their defences, which now form their most apparent feature, vary considerably in terms of both their architecture and of their configuration on the terrain. Whilst not necessarily of chronological importance, such variations lend support to hypotheses of diversity of function as well as of date.

An imposing series of works, marked by sub-rectangular enclosures frequently displaying substantial signs of vitrification, is a characteristic type in the North-East (Feachem, 1966). Evidence from Angus and Inverness-shire, as well as from Green Cairn fort, Cairnton of Balbegno, Kincardine, suggests that they were constructed during the centuries around the transition from the Bronze Age to the Iron Age in the middle of the first millennium BC. These fused relics of former timber-laced defences can no longer be envisaged as a distinguishing characteristic of the forts of a population implacably opposed to the broch-builders of the North and West. It may be remarked that the distribution of such vitrified forts coincides in broad terms with that occupied by Pictish stones many centuries later.

If the oblong vitrified forts represent a class widely dispersed over North-East Scotland, other types appear to have a much more localised distribution. An example is offered by the stone-walled forts, best represented in the Garioch, and from there southwards towards the Dee. At the Barmekin of Echt, superficial examination suggests a constructional sequence in which a suite of ramparts with multiple entrances was replaced by a double circuit of dry-stone walls. There is no dating evidence available for such sites, and it is not impossible that the stone-walled enclosures continued in use into Pictish times.

Most of the forts of North-East Scotland are so categorised on account of their hill-top, and apparently defensive siting, rather than because of the military obstacle of their enveloping works. There are, however, other stone-walled or embanked enclosures, less obviously defensive in primary intent, which were probably used as farmsteads. In the lowlands, these are complemented by ditched enclosures, now apparent as cropmarks in the cereal fields in dry summers. Some show evidence of the former positions of stockades or palisades on the inner margins of their ditches. Beyond suggesting that their likely period of use spans the first millennia BC and AD, it would be hazardous in the absence of excavation evidence to attribute such sites solely to the Picts or to their predecessors.

One site dominates the early fortifications of the North-East in terms of size and complexity. This is the fort which surrounds the 563m high summit of Tap o' Noth, near Rhynie. Visually, the most impressive feature of this hill is the well-preserved vitrified fort

Oblique sunlight highlights probable house platforms and the outer wall below the vitrified fort on the summit of Tap o' Noth, near Rhynie.

which crowns the summit. This massive work is possibly datable to around the middle of the first millennium BC. However, a much less imposing stone-edged terrace encircles the hill at lower altitude, and encloses an area of about 20 ha in extent. Within the area so defined may be seen a series of levelled platforms which may have formed the stances for timber roundhouses and other structures. Well over 200 of these can be recognised. Through these strings and clusters of platforms wend a series of tracks. It is certainly possible that this settlement, now cloaked in crowberries and heather, once represented the major settlement of the Caledonians north of the Mounth, but dating is again hazardous. Few finds have been made on the hill, and the recorded ones come from the skirts below this outer enclosure rather than from the enclosed area: one of the 'Donside' terrets (no 13), glass beads including a 'Pictish' example (no 29), and two sherds of Roman samian pottery are the potentially diagnostic items.

For what they are worth, these finds may suggest use of the site in the first few centuries AD, making Tap o' Noth a local equivalent for native forts, such as Traprain Law in East Lothian, which, in the occupied zone of Roman Scotland, certainly flourished during this period. However, it is also possible that this remarkably high settlement may be considerably older, belonging to perhaps the beginning of the first millennium BC, before the worsening of the climate accelerated, rendering life on so exposed a hill-side rather more uncomfortable. The fact that some of the platforms appear to lie below tumble from the vitrified fort on the summit may lend a modicum of support to this latter hypothesis.

Tap o' Noth is, in terms of its scale, an enigma. Four times larger than the next biggest fort in the region—that recently-discovered on the Hill of Newleslie—it would conventionally be ascribed to the period immediately prior to the Roman advance. However, whilst an earlier date is clearly possible, it is also feasible that this massive site is a testimony to the centralizing tendencies which pushed the tribes of northern Scotland into acting in concert against Agricola. Despite the apparent severity of their defeat, such processes may have continued thereafter, eventually to give rise to the amalgam of peoples known as the Picts.

The Roman Army, as a year-round garrison force, appears never to have extended its range beyond Strathmore, where the northernmost permanent fortification in the Empire is recorded at Stracathro (Breeze, 1982). Military strategy of the period was such that we must imagine patrols venturing out from the fort, and its southern neighbours. North of Stracathro, however, all the known Roman sites are testimonies of the Army on campaign in the form of temporary camps built to enclose the tented accommodation of legionaries and auxiliaries. These extend almost to the Moray Firth, at Bellie, on the East side of the Spey, though this, the most northerly camp, is not accepted by all commentators. Whilst it is tempting to interpret this line of camps as the relics of a single campaign, perhaps that of Agricola, variations in size and proportions as well as in details of entrance arrangements do not favour this interpretation (Maxwell, 1981). The most likely campaigns are those of Agricola in the mid-80s AD and of the Imperial Army of Septimius Severus in the early third century. It is nonetheless possible that these camps include some which were constructed during manoeuvres, either less important or less glorious, for which no historical record exists. From our point of view, concerned as we are with the subsequent emergence of the Picts, it is important to note that the military successes in the field were never consolidated thereafter. North-East Scotland was excluded from the benefits and disadvantages of incorporation into the Roman Empire. Coins and other small objects indicate that contact nonetheless existed (Curle, 1932; Robertson, 1970). Some of this material may have appeared in the North as a result of trading links, however informal, rather than as a by-product of raiding. Some items may not have reached this part of the country until after the Roman withdrawal.

But it would be excessive to see in this failure to consolidate military success an indication of indomitable valour on the part of the Caledonians or the Picts. Viewed dispassionately from the centre of power on the Tiber, this northern zone is likely to have seemed remote, hard to garrison, and harder to convert to a civil province: the costs of achieving these ends are likely to have outweighed such benefits as might have accrued to the Imperial Treasury. Whilst the great battle of Mons Graupius may well have been fought north of the Mounth—Bennachie (St Joseph, 1978) and the Pass of Grange represent possible locations (Keppie, 1981)—nothing suggests any radical change in this area over the succeeding centuries. Late Iron Age metalwork shows links with areas further south, and some of it may have belonged to refugees who moved northward to escape Roman domination (MacGregor, 1976), bringing with them that strand of Celtic speech which was to subsist alongside the now-incomprehensible Pictish (Jackson, 1955). But it is equally possible that such 'Celtic stock' was already present centuries before the Agricolan advance.

A brief history: from Mons Graupius to Macbeth

'. . . a nation still then uncultured and accustomed only to the hitherto semi-naked Picts and Hibernians as their sole enemies . . .'

Eumenius *Panegyric to Constantine* AD 297

The Classical world in which the above statement was penned was dominated by the Empire of Rome, an empire which, whilst still immensely powerful, was no longer expanding as it had done in previous centuries. Our Picts thus surface as one of a set of peoples, living outwith the Roman domain, but periodically coming into contact with it. Since the reasons for contact being recorded were more usually to do with frontier problems and conflicts than with more peaceful arrangements, it is precisely about the former that we are told. Our later sources, too, again written furth of Pictland, record for the most part major affairs of state—the royal succession, battles and so on—and the triumphs and set-backs of the new Church. Thus our historical record is partial, both in the sense of 'incomplete' and 'biased'. It provides the broad brush strokes, but little of the fine line work.

Before this reference to the Picts, our knowledge of the political map of Scotland north of the Forth is dominated by that provided, however insecurely, in the *Geography* of Ptolemy (Richmond, 1958; Rivet and Smith, 1979). This shows the area as the territory of a number of tribes, of whom the most extensive appear to have been the Caledonii. Some of the tribal names present are not certainly Celtic, which, given the survival of a non-Indo-European language in this region

in later times, is not surprising. In later classical sources, the usual political configuration recorded for this part of Scotland is one dominated by two names, one the Caledonii (or a recognisable variation thereof) and the other more changeable. These may well represent confederacies of native tribes, such as were established in the face of Roman aggression in the first century AD. After 297, usage becomes rather more variable. For example, Incertus, writing in 310, described 'Caledonians and other Picts'.

The periodic irruptions of these peoples, either singly or in alliances, southward, produced not only physical destruction in the Roman province, but provoked retaliatory attacks. It is on such barbarian campaigns that some of the Donside terrets (nos 12 & 13) may have been discarded south of Hadrian's Wall. Memories of such unsettled times find their echo in the first 'British history', that of Gildas. Writing about 540 AD, but referring to events a century or so before (Morris, 1975), he states:

"As the Romans made to go home, there emerged from the coracles that had carried them across the sea valleys, the foul hordes of Scots and Picts like dark throngs of worms who wriggle out of fissures in the rock when the sun is high and the weather grows warm. They were to some extent different in their customs but were in perfect accord in their greed for bloodshed, and were more willing to cover their villainous faces with hair than their private parts and neighbouring regions with clothes . . .'

The 'foul hordes' of our title clearly made an unfavourable impression on the sub-Roman world of southern Britain. It is possible to suggest that the episode recorded here may link up with the exploits of an early Pictish king—Drust, son of Erp—who is stated in the Pictish *King Lists* to have 'fought a hundred battles', and who may have lived in the first half of the fifth century. However, it is by no means certain that many of the early Pictish kings, named in the *Lists*, are not other than later inventions, added to bolster the pedigree of the monarchy. The reference to a hundred battles also reeks of heroic exaggeration.

If accepted in an unqualified way, the succession of Pictish kings would stretch well back into prehistory, beginning with some reigns of Old Testament length (Anderson, 1973, 77-84). Contrastingly, the first independently-recorded king is Bridei mac Maelchon, mentioned in the Annals and described by Columba's biographer as 'rex potentissimus'. The use of this adjective suggests a graded monarchy, perhaps akin to the Irish model, in which sub-kings with more restricted territorial holdings were also represented.

This record refers to the mid sixth century, and from then on it is sources in the Irish and Northumbrian worlds which provide the bulk of our references. The establishment of Fergus mac Erc in Dalriata, before 501, saw the transfer of the centre of the Scotic kingdom from Ulster to Argyll, and represented a transfer of power which had been preceded by Scotic colonisation of uncertain duration (Duncan, 1975). The subsequent expansion of this Scotic kingdom brought it into conflict with its neighbours, including the Cruithne, the word the Scots used for the Picts. Part of this expansion may be attributable to prosaic causes, such as land hunger, but undoubtedly the need for military successes to consolidate the monarchy's hold and prestige goods to lubricate internal political arrangements within the Scotic kingdom are likely reasons for expansion into adjoining territories. Entries in the Annals briefly announce a catalogue of such events. Thus, the *Annals of Tigernach,* for a year *c* 559 (Anderson, 1922, 21):

"Death of Gabran, Domngart's son, King of Scots. Flight of the Scots before Brude, Maelchon's son, King of the Picts".

The subsequent visit of Columba to King Brude (or Bridei) a few years later may, as recounted elsewhere, have been diplomatic as much as pastoral in intention. This took place somewhere near the River Ness. The then new monastery at Iona was close to Pictish territory, and one source suggests that the land grant to found it came from the Pictish monarch. Relative calm seems to have prevailed in relations between Pict and Scot for the next few years. Contrastingly, the Annals of Ulster mention internal conflicts amongst the Scots in the late 560s.

King Bridei's status at the time of Columba's visit is not spelt out for us. Clearly, there were other petty kings under his power: instructions to a 'regulus' in Orkney were issued during Bridei's negotiations with the Irish aristocrat. Whether Bridei's power extended over the entire Pictish domain is perhaps more debatable. Whilst the *King Lists* only cite one monarch at a time, the duality of Northern and Southern Pictland, intermittently mentioned in some sources, should be borne in mind. Furthermore, Pictland at its most extensive covered a diversity of terrain across which communications have never been easy, and there is perhaps reason to question the degree to which a central power was able in reality to control a series of territorial units which extended from perhaps the head-waters of the Forth to the Northern Isles. Echoes of the existence of a series of provinces are provided by both the Pictish regnal lists, and by the *De Situ Albanie,* a twelfth century document. These sources point to seven subdivisions, each attributed to one of the sons of Cruithne, who is portrayed as the father of the Picts. As translated by Skene, quoted by Anderson (1922, cxvi), one version reads:

"Now this land was divided anciently by seven brothers into seven parts. Of these, the principal is Angus with Mearns, so named after Oengus, the eldest of the brothers. And the second part is Athole and Gowrie. The third part is Strathearn with Montieth. The fourth of the parts is Fife with Fothreff; and the fifth part is Mar, with Buchan. The sixth is Moray and Ross. The seventh part is Caithness . . ."

The regional names given in this extract represent the presumed later equivalents of the seven brothers' mythical domains. These were known by other names (eg Fidach, probably for Moray), which are given at the head of the *King Lists.*

Even in Bridei's time, there are indications that the king had sometimes to fight to retain control of some of these provinces. In later times, for example in the second quarter of the eighth century, there was considerable internal disruption within Pictland, which may also reflect differing provincial allegiances.

For the better part of a century after Columba's time, the Picts seem to have been able to check the expansion of the Scots. A decade after the events on the Ness, the emergence of Aidan after a disputed succession within the royal house, saw him legitimised as King of Dalriata by Columba in 574. A bloody and ruthless policy against his neighbours led Aidan to campaign in the Orkneys in 580, but his defeat by the newly-emergent power of Northumbria in 604 and that of his grandson and successor Domnall Brecc, at the hands of the Strathclyde British in Strathcarron in 643 (Anderson, 1922, 166), may have dissipated Scotic pressure on the Pictish heartland. However, there is little secure information on Scoto-Pictish relations at this period. Miller (1980, 320) has suggested that Aidan's intervention in Orkney may have been as an ally of the Picts. Against that, there is the possibility of a battle between Picts and Scots in Circhenn—the Mearns—in 598, although it is likely that this record is corrupt (Anderson, 1973, 146). Another entry in the Annals describes Eochaid, Aidan's son and immediate successor, as 'rex Pictorum' (Anderson, 1973, 151 and fn 141): this title may refer to a province of Pictland other than Fortriu, the kings of which are those normally recorded.

The next main external threat to the Picts was to come from a new quarter. The *Annals of Tigernach* mention, under the year 657, the death of Talorcan, Eanfrith's son, the King of the Picts (Anderson, 1922, 176). Eanfrith was clearly Anglian, as his name suggests: that his son should have been King of Picts need occasion no surprise, given the matrilinear system which still characterised the Pictish succession, and which frequently produced kings whose fathers were members of other royal houses. This event would however have disrupted Pictish relations with the Anglians, who had established themselves in Lothian by the 640s. About 658, the Northumbrian king, Oswiu, invaded Southern Pictland and defeated the Pictish army (Anderson, 1922, 175), thereby annexing an unknown fraction of Pictish territory to his kingdom. This event may have had profound ramifications, which may be perceived in both the subsequent development of Christianity in Pictland, discussed below, and perhaps also in art. For a generation, Southern Pictland remained in Anglian hands: an attempt by the Picts to liberate their territory appears to have foundered in 676.

The next powerful King of the Picts to emerge was Bridei mac Bili, son of a king of Strathclyde, first recorded in 682 as the destroyer of the Orkneys. The siege of Dunnottar recorded in the previous year, and mentioned below, may be an indication of this new

The mediaeval castle of Dunnottar occupies the likely site of the Pictish fort of duin Foither.

monarch re-establishing his hold over parts of his domain, but this is only speculation. By the middle of the decade, the Anglians had been ousted from Southern Pictland. The decisive battle took place at Nechtansmere, near Forfar, on 20th May, 685 (Anderson, 1922, 192).

> "Egferth, who fought in a battle against his cousin, the King of Picts named Bridei, and there fell with the strength of his army, and the Picts and their King were victorious, and the English thugs never grew from the time of that battle to exact tribute from the Picts".
>
> Nennius, *Historia Brittonum*

The Anglians retreated south of the Forth, and their bishop, Trumwine, left Paenfahel, near that river.

Further hostilities are however recorded in 698 and 711. The Irish form of Christianity was re-established in Southern Pictland. Thereafter, the main centres of Pictish power seem to have been located essentially in Southern Pictland, perhaps largely because the king needed to be near the frontier over which he was most likely to lead his war-band. Scone, Dunkeld and Forteviot all appear to have been important in subsequent generations. The Annals increasingly refer to the Pictish monarch as King of Fortriu. Such was Bridei mac Bili's appellation on his death in 693 (Anderson, 1922, 193 and 200).

The beginning of the next century saw independent Pictland adopting the Romanised form of Christianity which, if established earlier, had been rejected along with Anglian domination at Nechtansmere. This occurred during the reign on Nechtan (706-724), and is discussed below. To what extent this re-orientation angered traditionalists is unknown, but the end of his reign was marked by considerable turmoil in Pictland. Nechtan entered a monastery in 724 (Anderson, 1922, 221), but the record in the *Annals of Tigernach* for 726 indicates that his successor, Drust, reigned only briefly:

'Drust was cast from the Kingdom of the Picts, and Alpin reigned in his stead.'

Alpin's name may be an early indication of the rise of Scotic interests in the Pictish royal line, but his hold on the kingship was short-lived. He was twice defeated in battle in 728:

'Battle of Moin-craibe amongst the Picts themselves. Angus and Alpin were they that fought this battle. And the rout was before Angus, and the son of Alpin was slain there; and Angus took authority.'

Annals of Tigernach, 728

It is possible that this battle took place at Moncrieffe Hill (Anderson, 1973, 177). The internal conflicts amongst the Picts were by no means over. Nechtan mac Derile, the same man as had previously retired, or been ousted, from the kingship, also fought with, and defeated Alpin.

'A pitiful battle between the Picts at Caislen-Credi: and the rout was on the same Alpin and his

territories and his men were all taken from him. And Nechtan, Derile's son, took the kingship of Fortriu.'

Annals of Tigernach, 728

Within a year, Oengus (Angus) defeated the depleted forces of Nechtan at a battle at Monith-Carno, sometimes identified with the Cairn o' Mounth, thereby consolidating his hold on Pictland. Despite this period of dynastic feuding, Pictland under Oengus emerges as the strongest kingdom of its day. Dunadd, capital of the Scots, was captured in 736 (Anderson, 1922, 233), and the beginning of the next decade saw Angus consolidating his hold over Dalriata after a victory over the Scots at Druimm-Cathmail in 741. Subsequent years saw him campaigning against the Strathclyde Britons, in 744, 750 (unsuccessfully), and, in concert with the Northumbrians, in 756. In the last campaign, the British capital at Dumbarton was captured, but the destruction of the Pictish army, a matter of a few days later, put paid to this period of Pictish expansionism. Oengus remained in control of his other territories until his death in 761.

This reign would appear to mark the high water mark of Pictish territorial aspirations. Significantly, the achievement is that of a king whose focus was clearly towards the South, and the implication that the North was becoming a backwater is there to be taken. However, it is salutary to bear in mind that the historical record is very incomplete and developments in the North were less likely to come to the attention of, still less to impinge on, the monastic communities in which these records were compiled.

The later 8th century may be considered as a period in which the Pictish kingdom went into a slow decline. A battle in Fortriu in 768 marked the resumption of Scoto-Pictish hostilities after a generation (Anderson, 1973, 189). Further internal conflicts and dynastic feuds appear in the literature, as in 789. The Picts may have retained a measure of control of Dalriata until about this stage and indeed Conall, once a King of the Picts, and recorded as the loser of a battle with Constantine in that year, may have reigned thereafter in Dalriata. In 782 a Pictish King is described as reigning *citra Monoth*, indicating that his domain did not extend beyond the hills of the Mounth.

The appearance of the Vikings or 'gentiles' from the end of the century further disrupted the apparently-precarious existence of the Kingdom of the Picts. Frequent raids are recorded from 794.

By the middle of the ninth century, the independent kingdom of the Picts was at an end. In the earlier part of that century, Pictish kings appear to have reigned simultaneously in Dalriata and Pictland. These included Constantine, styled 'Custatin mac Fergusa rex Fortrenn' at his death in 820. In 839, the *Annals of Ulster* record the death of his successor, Oengus II, called Eoganan in Irish sources:

> 'A battle of the gentiles against the men of Fortriu (Picts), and in it fell, Eoganan . . . and others fell almost without number'.

Clearly the Picts, once so powerful, were unable to counter the ramifications of this new threat. But it would be simplistic to account for the decline of the Picts purely in terms of external aggression. The demise of the royal martilinear system early in the 9th century—the first possible case of son succeeding father to the throne occurs in 780 (Anderson, 1973, 166)—appears to have happened at a time and in a way to favour the Scots, who themselves were under considerable pressure from Scandinavian raids. Thus a Scotic prince, Kenneth mac Alpin, emerged as King of the Picts and Scots in 843, and his dynasty was able to resist subsequent Pictish claimants.

The Scottish take-over of the political intitutions and centres in southern Pictland appears all the more complete because of the spread thereafter of Gaelic place-names. Some names, particularly those beginning with 'Pit-' are composites, with Gaelic second elements, and suggest the retention of a Pictish land unit. These are, somewhat surprisingly, common as far south as Fife. If the separate identity of the Picts disappeared, the resultant kingdom was sufficiently strong to check Viking expansionism. The church survived, and may have contributed to the process of assimilation of Pict with Scot.

The Annals indicate that a major pre-occupation of ninth-century monarchs was resisting Viking raids. In 858, for example, the Danes are described as wasting Pictland 'to Clunie and Dunkeld' (Anderson, 1922, 288) in the year of Kenneth mac Alpin's death. The following decades are marked by similar assaults, usually, it would appear, originating from the West, and striking into the district still called Fortriu. For a generation or two, the kings were still styled as 'of the Picts', thus Donald, who died in 862, is described as 'rex Pictorum'. The first case of a monarch being called 'ri Alban', King of Alba, in the *Annals of Ulster* occurs in 899 (Anderson, 1973, 197). An instance of the replacement of earlier practices is indicated in the previous decade, when Church-State relations were reorganised according to Scotic principles (Anderson, 1973, 198).

However, as Duncan has remarked (1975, 111), the emergence of a single large kingdom covering a substantial proportion of the Scottish mainland offers a marked contrast to the internal political divisions within both England and Ireland in the mid-ninth century. The measure of control actually achieved by the monarchy, particularly in areas where Gaelic-speaking landowners may have been few in number, is likely not to have been complete. Territorial reorganisation is suggested by the appearance of a new series of regional names—'Moray' for earlier 'Fidach', for example. But the survival of Pictish names—toiseach, mormaer—for ranks in the aristocratic and administrative superstructure is of considerable interest.

In contrast to the earlier period, for which direct references to the North-East are almost completely absent, the tenth and eleventh centuries contain records of various events which took place in this area. They may be read to suggest that the Kings of Alba, who were extending their territory southward, faced considerable resistance in the broad area then referred to as Moray. For much of this period, it is possible that Moray was effectively autonomous. The 'Kings' of Moray traced their descent from a different branch of the original Irish settlers of Dalriata than did the mac Alpin dynasty. We can only surmise the extent to which this dynastic feud was matched by a different degree of 'Pictish survivals' in the more northerly area. It has however been suggested that some of the later Pictish art from this area may be viewed as a last gasp of defiant independence.

Southern kings certainly seem to have met their deaths in the North with surprising regularity. Donald I perished in Moray, possibly at Forres, in 900. In 954, variant traditions indicate that Malcolm was killed by the men of Moray at Ulum, or possibly at Fetteresso in the Mearns (Anderson, 1922, 452-3). A decade later, King Indulf died, this time at the hands of Vikings, at the mouth of a river—either the Cowie near Stonehaven, or at Cullen, in Banffshire. King Dubh was killed by his successor at Forres in 966, and Kenneth II met his death in an elaborate trap, according to later tradition, at Fettercairn in 995.

The reign of Macbeth in the middle of the next century marks the zenith of the Moray dynasty. From the death of Duncan in 1040, certainly in the diocese of Moray and possibly at Pitgaveny (Anderson, 1922, 581, fn 7), until his defeat at Lumphanan in 1057, Macbeth appears to have ruled south of the Mounth as well. The death of his son, Lulach, at Essie in Strathbogie in 1058 put paid to the possibility of continuing northern control over the south. But thirty years later, Maelsnechtai, Lulach's son, was still styled 'King of Moray' at his death.

Older cults and Christianity

The introduction of Christianity is likely to have had its profoundest effects in aspects of life far removed from the material culture which forms one of the mainstays of our evidence. This is not to suggest that the chapel sites, sculpture and religious metalwork are insignificant, but rather to indicate that acceptance of the new religion may have provoked more substantial consequences in aspects of social and political life,

which are far more difficult to detect in our surviving source materials. Equally, whilst some documentary evidence is available, this was produced exclusively in a Christian milieu, and thus the possibility of bias in that direction is also likely. The acceptance of the new order by a king and his entourage did not necessarily entail wholesale adoption by the wider populace. Accordingly, it is possible that burial practices in particular may have continued unaltered, particularly in places remote from the foci of the new religion.

These prefatory remarks serve to suggest that the adoption of Christianity over an area as extensive as Pictland is unlikely to have been accomplished quickly, and it is in the archaelogical record that we have the best chance of perceiving indications of the continuation of older practices. As that set of evidence stands at present, there is little to suggest a wholesale change in either burial rites or in the focus of ritual

Cropmarks of a complex enclosure at Barflat, near Rhynie, may be contemporary with several Pictish stones recovered from the vicinity.

activities during the period in question, although our lack of chronological control must be admitted at the outset. Like many aspects of Pictish 'culture' in the North-East, the practices used for the disposal of the dead show long pedigrees, without us necessarily being able to demonstrate that the traditions are unbroken. For example, a burial, possibly a cremation, in a short cist at Easterton of Roseisle represents a rite established in the Bronze Age. In this case, however, the cist differed somewhat from the usual form, more especially in the incorporation of a Class I Pictish stone, perhaps datable as early as the sixth century AD, although other experts would prefer a later date. Further south in Scotland, a series of cemeteries of long cists, enclosing extended inhumations, is often attributed to early Christian communities. There appear to be no equivalents of these north of the Mounth, where the occasional long cist burial, as at Garbeg in Inverness-shire, may have taken place as early as the final centuries BC (Wedderburn and Grime, 1975), although this assessment requires different monuments at the site to have been contemporary. Moreover, two series of rectangular funerary monuments invite comparisons with pre-Roman Iron Age burial practices further South. One of these involves burial within a rectilinear enclosure, now defined by a small ditch detectable in aerial survey, but once covered by a square barrow (Maxwell, 1983, fig 25). A parallel for this tradition in stone is

Square and circular marks in the middle of this photograph possibly define a cemetery of Pictish date at the Hills of Boyndie, near Banff.

more exclusively North Scottish, and includes sites such as Tillytarmont, near the confluence of the Isla and the Deveron. This set of sites has been discussed by Ashmore (1980). It is possible that some examples had functions other than burial.

Recognisably Pictish material has been recovered from a number of sites in the North-East at which previous ritual activity is indicated. Many of these sites date back to the second millennium BC at least,

although it would be unsafe to envisage their continuing sanctity across the intervening centuries. Nonetheless, the propinquity of Pictish sculpture to earlier prehistoric ritual sites, as at Broomend of Crichie near Inverurie, and Ardlair in the Garioch, perhaps occurs too frequently to be dismissed as the operation of chance. Rather different cases are offered by the context of the Gaulcross hoard (see no 25) and perhaps by the signs of Pictish activity in the Sculptor's Cave at Covesea on the Moray Firth coast, discussed below, where, earlier, Bronze Age, rituals are attested (Shepherd, 1983).

The first intimations of the appearance of Christianity in the territory that was subsequently to become Scotland occur in the context of the late Roman world (Thomas, 1967; 1971; 1982). It is likely that the earliest of the historically-documented churchmen, Ninian, was sent to minister to a pre-existing Christian community in the far South-West of the country, since references to him as a bishop suggest the earlier establishment of a territorial see dependent on Whithorn. A bishop would not have been sent into heathen lands. Direct evidence for the presence of early Christians in southern Scotland is offered by a number of sculptured crosses and inscribed stones, the latter displaying epigraphic evidence characteristic of the fifth and sixth centuries AD. At the Catstane, now within the perimeter of Turnhouse airport, such a stone is associated with a long cist cemetery, of the type alluded to above (Cowie, 1978).

Bede, the main early source on Ninian, also describes him as having converted the Southern Picts to Christianity. Whilst some authors have enthusiastically endorsed this mention, and have argued for the establishment of the Roman form of Christianity quite far North, more recent commentators (Thomas, 1971; Donaldson, 1972; Duncan, 1975) have tended to take a more sanguine view. This stems partly from the description of Ninian as a bishop, as well as the fact that precocious intimations of the new religion, for example in the form of long cist cemeteries, do not extend over all of southern Pictland. Indeed, Thomas has suggested that an enclave of Pictland may have extended south of the Forth at this time (1967; 1982). However, supporting evidence for early Christianity—or at least its former presence—in southern Pictland is offered by Saint Patrick's letter to Coroticus (a king of the Strathclyde Britons) and his followers. Datable to the mid-fifth century AD, this letter condemns the practice of selling slaves—particularly Christians, and especially to the Picts. These latter, whom he castigates for sinning 'openly, grievously and shamelessly', are described as 'utterly iniquitous, evil and apostate'. The backsliding indicated by the last-mentioned term is indicative of at least the former presence of Christianity in Pictish areas by about 450AD, but there is no evidence that the new religion had been implanted north of the Mounth by this date. Furthermore, no subsequent author restricts later missions to the northern part of Pictland, so that this north-south divide as regards the adoption of Christianity depends almost entirely on the testimony of Bede.

Whatever the extent and success of Ninianic activity, it is clear that the conversion of the remainder of Pictland occurred both at a later date and from a different source. Bede offers the historical framework:

"In the year of our Lord 565, when Justin the Younger succeeded Justinian and ruled as Emperor of Rome, a Priest and Abbot named Columba, distinguished by his monastic habit and life, came from Ireland to preach the Word of God in the provinces of the Northern Picts..."

History of the English Church and People

Columba, born in Donegal in 521, was thus a man of considerable standing when he came to Scotland and extended the sphere of the Irish form of Christianity northward from the new monastery established on Iona in 563. This form of Christianity developed along different lines from that of the Roman tradition, essentially as a result of isolation rather than of a deliberate schism. In the longer term, doctrinal differences from the Roman church would contribute to its loss of ground and eventual demise, but in the short term the organizational characteristics of Irish Christianity meant that it was well-adapted to establish itself in new areas, particularly where population was scattered. The hierarchial organisation of the Roman church was dependent on bishops who were, at least in theory, appointed by the Pope. The bishop was keeper of both discipline and doctrine, with authority over each religious house and priest within the prescribed territory of his diocese. Contrastingly, the Columban church was monastic in structure, and controlled by abbots. Bishops were much less significant. The abbots, sometimes drawn from the cadet branches of the aristocracy, were elected to the office, and were responsible both for the running of the monastery and for sending out monks to minister to communities further afield. Thus these monasteries were not closed, contemplative communities (Bulloch, 1971, 35). An eremitic and ascetic tradition contributed to the spread of this form of Christianity, although it is often difficult to pinpoint the date at which the faith reached particular areas.

Columba is given sole credit for the conversion of the Picts in the writing of his biographer, Adamnan, a later abbot of Iona, whose account was compiled in the 690s. This may be due in part to scanty and awkward evidence, but is more likely to be attributed to Adamnan's desire to laud the achievements of his predecessor. The documentary evidence only records one certain visit by Columba to Pictland and that was essentially confined, in geographical terms, to the Ness valley. This mission took place in 565, and involved meetings between Columba and King Bridei mac Maelchon. Much of Adamnan's account consists of evidence of Columba's holiness (Henderson, 1975) as illustrated by victories in magic contests with Bridei's father-in-law, who was described as a druid or magi. Amongst these is the first record of the Loch Ness Monster. Various sites have been suggested as the site of Bridei's *domus regia* or 'palace', including Craig Phadrig, which is a vitrified fort near Inverness, that town itself, and the site of Castle Urquhart on the western shore of Loch Ness. Whilst Columba was able to secure free passage for missionaries through the Pentland Firth (Anderson and Anderson, 1961) and carried out conversions (although not apparently that of King Bridei), his aims may have been, in present-day terms, primarily diplomatic rather than religious. Pictish-Scotic hostility seems to have declined for a generation thereafter.

Although Columba is recorded as having made subsequent journeys, during one of which he converted a Pict on Skye, he is not certainly reported as having come to the North-East. This latter area, even if nominally Christian, is not likely to have been subject to widespread evangelising immediately after the events of 565. We know little of how the practicalities of conversion were achieved, and it would clearly overstate the evidence to suggest that North-East Scotland was fully Christian by 600. Unfortunately, Columba seems to have 'swallowed up into his own fame all the works of his predecessors, companions and contemporaries, and deprived generations of pioneers and missionaries of their just fame' (MacBain, 1886, 150). The names of some of these early churchmen do survive, albeit shadowily. Their lives and works have however often been amended by medieval scribes desirous of making these earlier activists fit in with the course of subsequent developments (Galbraith, 1982).

Thus the record in the *Aberdeen Breviary* that Saint Nathalan, who died in 678, was a bishop returned from Rome, squares ill with Columban missionary expansion from Iona and its sister houses in the West. Bishops as community leaders would only have been appropriate to this area after the adoption of the Roman form of Christianity in the early eighth century, and it is possible that some subsequent scribe elevated Nathalan to this rank after the changeover. Nathalan is attributed with the foundation of the church at Tullich on Deeside amongst others. Here archaeological evidence would tend to support an early foundation, as numbers of small inscribed crosses, referred to as 'primary grave markers, have been found.

The first saint recorded as having been active in Buchan is Saint Drostan. His dates, and much else about him, are now uncertain, since subsequent records, made in the Abbey of Deer, seem designed to 'age' its foundation. Drostan is reputed to have died in the mid-sixth century, before the Columban mission! Land grants at Deer and at Dundarg are dedicated to

Various defensive phases can be seen on top of the promontory of Dundarg, near Rosehearty. The likeliest 'Dark Age' defence is marked by the ditch faintly visible in the walled garden of the modern house.

this saint. A marginal note in the Book of Deer records the grant of the land at Dundarg to Drostan by a local Pictish mormaer, Bédé. At Deer, the site of the initial monastery is uncertain, although low-lying land near the Ugie may have been preferred to the site subsequently chosen for the later Abbey. It is possible that entries in the Irish Annals for 622 and 678 in which reference is made to a place called Neir, refer to this establishment (Henderson, 1967).

Amongst other early saints to whom foundations in the North-East are attributed are St Moluag (Mo-Luoc) and St Maelrubha. The earlier of the two, Moluag, was the founder of the monastery at Lismore, a sister house of Iona. Moluag was active in the same century as Columba, and is reputed to have established churches at Mortlach near Dufftown, and at Clova and Kildrummy in Strathdon. Direct evidence of early structures at these sites is lacking, although both Clova, and Mortlach, once the seat of a bishopric (MacDonald and Laing, 1970, 142-3) were to be incorporated into the diocese of Aberdeen in the twelfth century (Easson and Cowan, 1976).

Maelrubha was the founder of the Columban community established at Appurcrossan, nowadays Applecross, and was active in the years around 700. His connection with the North-East is based almost exclusively on dedicatory evidence, much of which may be regarded as suspect. He may however be credited with the foundation of one site in the valley of the Isla at Keith (Simpson, 1925).

No indisputable trace of any early foundation remains visible on the ground today. It is possible that the remains of early structures, most likely of wood, lie buried beneath medieval and later buildings erected on the same sites. A clearer indication of the spread of Christianity may be offered by the surviving distribution of sculpture of several types.

The varieties of sculpture with which we are here concerned are Pictish stones of Classes II and III, and simple incised crosses, including small examples known as 'primary grave markers'. The Class II and III stones are overtly Christian in so far as they portray the Cross, although in the case of the Class II sculpture various of the arguably pre-Christian symbols, discussed below, are also retained. Compared to Angus and adjacent areas, the number of sites with Class II and Class III stones in the North-East in not great. Some fourteen sites have produced such cross-slabs. They are concentrated in the Laigh of Moray and in the Howe of Cromar, although survivors in other fertile zones of Aberdeenshire, north Kincardine and upper Banffshire suggest that the distribution was once more widespread. Buchan lacks monuments of this type, and also incised crosses, with the exceptions of a Pictish stone re-used for an incised cross at Deer, now lost, and a fragment of a late cross-shaft from the Ythan valley at Fyvie.

The origins of incised crosses have been discussed by Thomas (1971). He places them within the Irish monastic tradition, thereby suggesting that they could have been made in the North-East in the century after the Columban mission. The incised crosses in this area

The incised crosses at Tullich Church, near Ballater.

have been listed by Anderson and Allen (1903), Ritchie (1915) and Simpson (1925; 1943).

Compared to the foundation traditions rehearsed above, solid historical documentation is less than fulsome (Easson and Cowan, 1976). The only establishment acceptable to these authors as definitely of Columban character was at Turriff. It, and Aberdour, may have been 7th century foundations

21

(Cowan, 1975, 18). It is interesting to note that the finest piece of early religious metalwork from the North-East, the Brecbennoch of Saint Columba—otherwise known as the Monymusk Reliquary—was associated with the heritors of the neighbouring lands of Forglenn on the Deveron.

There are some ten sites in the North-East which have sufficient documentary evidence to make the establishment of an early religious community likely. At some of these, sculptural evidence lends support. A provisional list might include Birnie (MacDonald and Laing, 1970, 140-1), Deer, Fordoun, Kinkell, Monymusk, Mortlach and Tarland. If this evidence is juxtaposed with the remainder of the sculpture, the resultant distribution berokens the presence of Christian communities scattered fairly widely over the North-East by the ninth century AD. A notable gap in the evidence occurs in the lowlands between the Deveron and the Spey.

Both the scale and the nature of the conversions to the new faith are ill-documented. Bede quotes a letter, sent by Pope Gregory to Abbot Mellitus in 601, which, whilst referring to the English, lends support to the idea that the replacement of former practices elsewhere may have been less than total:

> "We have come to the conclusion that the temples of the idols among the people should on no account be destroyed, but the temples themselves are to be aspersed with holy water, altars set up in them, and relics deposited there . . . In this way, we may hope that the people, seeing that their temples are not destroyed, may abandon their error and, flocking more readily to their accustomed resorts, may come to know and adore their true God.'

History of the English Church and People

To what extent it is this practice that led to the establishment of chapels next to stone circles is a moot point. But it may also have contributed to the creation of numbers of holy wells at what were previously springs of pagan significance, for water appears to have been of significance not only to the cults of the Celts (Ross, 1967) but also to the Picts, if we can attach similar undercurrents to reports of the ritual drowning of prisoners.

The Irish form of Christianity held sway in North-East Scotland until the early eighth century. By that stage, taking a wider view, it was on the retreat. Christian Northumbria, to which Irish clerics had been invited to establish a monastery at Lindisfarne in 635, had subsequently fallen into line with the Roman faith re-introduced into Britain by Saint Augustine at the end of the sixth century. This realignment was the outcome of the important synod, held at Whitby in 663, where matters of dispute between the two strands of the faith were debated.

The end of that decade, following the expansion of the Angles into eastern Scotland from the 630s, saw Wilfred described as Bishop of York, the Northumbrians and the Picts. A generation later, the Picts reversed the northward expansion of the temporal power of the Anglians at the great battle of Nechtansmere. Although the Anglian bishopric established at Paenfahel on the Forth did not survive this check, a generation later, Nechtan mac Derile, King of the Picts, sought help on doctrinal matters from the increasingly powerful monastic centres of Northumbria, in the person of Abbot Ceolfrith. Ceolfrith's response, once translated for Nechtan, contributed to the eclipse of the Irish monastic tradition in Pictland and the decline of Iona from 717. Whilst Pictland was now more open to religious influences emanating from the South, the replacement was far from total.

Subsequent re-orientation of the Irish church, and increasing Scotic influences in Pictland, meant that new monastic centres continued to be established. Whilst these may have copied their procedural and other arrangements from the Roman church of Northumbria, the later sculpture displays continuing influences from the West. Examples of this can be seen in the fragments from Kineddar (nos 30 & 31). However, Nechtan's decision to build a church 'in the

Roman manner'—that is to say, in stone—brought Northumbrian masons to Scotland.

In contrast to the earlier Irish Christian organisation, a pattern of territorial sees may have been established in Pictland from the 8th century, perhaps including Abernethy from the reign of Nechtan. Kilrymont (now St Andrews) from the reign of King Oengus, and Dunkeld by 850, and perhaps from the reign of King Constantine, are further examples.

Throughout this period, the monasteries were sustained in substantial part by the grant of lands by local aristocrats (like the mormaer noted above in connection with St Drostan) and by receiving privileged treatment with respect to woodland and other natural resources. Such grants are recorded in Adamnan's *Life of Columba,* and in the marginal notes on the *Book of Deer,* of about tenth century date. However, the discovery of a spectacular hoard of silver at Saint Ninian's Isle in Shetland in 1958 (O'Dell, 1960; Small *et al,* 1973), suggests that the church was also interested in acquiring portable secular wealth, since the objects do not appear, despite earlier suggestions, to have been of ecclesiastical significance. The church by the end of our period was perhaps less otherworldly that it had been in its earliest pioneering days.

Pictish settlement in the North-East: the archaeology

In the restricted sense in which Alcock (1981 a,b) promotes the term 'Early historic fortifications', only one is represented in the core of the North-East. His usage is conditional on the existence of historical records in which specific reference to a named site is made. The case in question is that of Dun Fo(i)ther.

The Annals of Ulster record sieges there in 681, and again thirteen years later, although the second entry may have been repeated in error (Anderson, 1922, 201). The *Old Scottish Chronicle* notes the destruction of 'opidum Fother' at the hands of the Vikings at the end of the 9th century. The coastal promontory site of the Castle Rock at Dunnottar, to the south of Stonehaven, is the most likely candidate for this name. Lying seaward of the easterly outliers of the hills of the Mounth, Dunnottar must be situated near to the former boundary between the Nothern and Southern Picts.

Otherwise, the only other documented fortification in the North of Pictland is the *regis munito* of Bridei, visited during Columba's mission to the Picts. No single site emerges as the agreed favourite for this role. Urquhart Castle, Craig Phadrig, and Inverness, all on, or close to, the River Ness, have their advocates: the evidence is reviewed by Henderson (1975) and Alcock (1981a).

Apart from these citations, evidenced for the use of fortifications is based essentially on archaeological data, drawn for the most part from coastal promontory sites. Exceptions to this rule include Craig Phadrig, near Inverness, and the Doune of Relugas on the

The remnants of the upper and lower forts, lies seaward of the modern village of Burghead.

border between Nairn and Moray. Four promontory sites on the south coast of the Moray Firth have produced indications of use during the period in question as the result of excavations since 1950.

Of these sites, Burghead, even in the severely damaged state to which it has now been reduced, is still the most impressive. As recorded in the 18th century, the promontory was defended by a triple set of ramparts and ditches drawn across its width. In the early 19th century, these were flattened prior to the construction of the village of Burghead. Behind the ramparts, and at slightly higher altitude, lay two enclosures. Each of these was defined by a wall, which also served to divide the apex of the promontory into a 'Lower' and an 'Upper' fort. Parts of these inner enclosures survive (Hogg, 1975, 146-7).

Since the middle of the 19th century, these defences have been examined periodically. The combined results of the excavations suggest considerable variation in the structure of this wall (Macdonald, 1862; Young, 1891, 1893; Small, 1969), but, in its most elaborate configuration, it would have represented a substantial undertaking in terms of both manpower and resources. Carefully constructed sandstone revetments delimited a wall some 8m thick, the core of which included a framework of oak timbers enveloped by rubble. This constructional technique was an old one, as such timber-laced ramparts have a long pedigree stretching back to the end of the Bronze Age in Scotland. A novelty in the Burghead wall was the use of iron nails about 20cm long to secure the junctions between the longitudinal and transversal timbers. Driving long iron spikes into oak beams must have necessitated much hard work, as well as representing, at least potentially, a considerable consumption of that metal. Recent excavations at Dundurn in Perthshire, on the southern fringes of Pictland, have demonstrated that the technique was also employed there (Alcock, 1980). Radiocarbon dates suggest that the Burghead wall was constructed around 400, and it is possible that this defence continued to be maintained until about 900 (Small, 1969; Edwards and Ralston, 1978).

Another impressive feature at Burghead, and indeed the only other recognisably Dark Age structure on the promontory, is the Bailey's Well, which lies in a portion of the fort now built over. Considerably modified since its discovery in the early 19th century, the well consisted of a subterranean chamber and tank, hewn out of the living rock, and approached by an irregular flight of steps. The elaborate nature of this arrangement, for which no Scottish equivalent is known, suggests that its function exceeded that of simply furbishing the inhabitants with water. During the 19th century, the tank and its accoutrements were taken to be a bath or a baptistery, on the basis of classical analogies (Young, 1890). Whatever function or combination of functions the Bailey's Well may have fulfilled, it serves as another indication of the former grandeur of the fort, which extended to about 3 ha in surface area.

The adequately-recorded small finds from Burghead give the impression, figuratively speaking, of the leavings from a rich man's table. The local antiquary, H W Young, remarked that 'coins, battle axes and spearheads', had in the past been given to English tourists (Young, 1891, 455). Much was undoubtedly lost during the building of the village and the modification of the neighbouring coastline.

Amongst the surviving material, pride of place must be accorded to the set of Class I stones, incised with bulls, discussed elsewhere (no 22), but sculptural elements also include parts of a corner-post shrine, decorated in Class II style, and indisputably Christian (Thomas, 1971, 152). This type of monument, of which the best-known mainland example comes from St Andrews, has been taken to suggest the former presence of a monastery in the vicinity (Henderson, 1975).

Other finds include a silver mount for a blast- or drinking-horn of Anglo-Saxon manufacture and 9th century date (Graham-Campbell, 1973), two of the North Scottish bead series sometimes called 'Pictish' (cf no 29), and a Roman melon bead (Curle, 1932, 296). The last mentioned object need not have arrived on the site until some time after the Roman period.

Amongst the other 'fortified' sites for which we have direct evidence of use in the Pictish period, not all necessarily possessed serviceable defences at this time. Craig Phadrig, near Inverness, for example, shows some signs of the refurbishment of the hill-top defences, originally of Iron Age date. More significant, however, are the discoveries of a mould and sherds of imported pottery during excavations there fifteen years ago. This pottery is a robust kitchen ware, probably manufactured in Atlantic France, and recovered from nearly 20 Dark Age sites in Scotland, as well from elsewhere in the British Isles (Thomas, 1981, 20-2). The mould—indicative of on-site metalworking—was for an escutcheon, the technical name given to decorated fitments attached to bronze hanging-bowls. These high-quality items have been most frequently recovered from Anglo-Saxon graves, of which Sutton Hoo is the most celebrated. Escutcheons displaying similarities to that which would have been formed in the Craig Phadrig mould are known as far south as Wessex. An association with penannular brooches in a hoard from Tummel Bridge, Perthshire, suggests a 5th or 6th century date for their manufacture (Longley, 1975, 16-8). This item is therefore indicative of Pictish participation in the mainstream of Dark Age luxury metalworking. Unfortunately, despite the apparent high status of these goods, the structural evidence from the recent excavations is restricted to a clay floor and some hearths—hardly enough to infer a royal residence.

Other inland sites with some indications of Pictish use are the Doune of Relugas in Moray and the Mither Tap o' Bennachie. The former is another vitrified fort, from which a variety of ringed pins (cf no 28) have been recovered (Fanning, 1983).

The granitic tor at the eastern end of Bennachie is another unexpected location for a fortified settlement, given the elevation (518m) of this conspicuous summit. When examined last century (MacLagan, 1875), the fort appears to have included a number of stone house foundations, but many of these are no longer readily visible. The most impressive feature is the great arc of walling enclosing a narrow terrace some 30m below the weathered tor on its eastern side.

This wall, now accompanied by an extensive spread of tumbled stone on its downslope side, is some 7m thick, and retains traces of a parapet, a wall-head walk, and

The tumbled walls of the fort encircle the rocky summit of the Mither Tap o' Bennachie.

a length of gallery behind its inner face towards its southern end. It is punctuated by a single entrance which is flanked by an external annexe on its north-east side. This is defined by a low wall of large boulders, and is approximately triangular in shape. Another stretch of walling isolates a small terrace below the tor on the western side. Within the fort thus defined, two tiers of scree on the eastern side of the rock outcrops probably represent debris from further defensive lines.

This fort differs markedly from most defended sites in the North-East in terms of both its lay-out and its siting. It is easier to parallel in the series of post-Roman forts, of which Dunadd, near Crinan Moss in Argyll, is perhaps the best-known. Classed as 'nuclear' or 'nucleated' since Stevenson's initial discussion of them (1949; Feachem, 1955), they are characterised by an interlocking series of enclosures whose shape and scale is conditioned by the form of the craggy outcrops which they enclose. Although Alcock's examination of a similar fort, at Dundurn in the south of Pictland, suggests that the structural sequence on them may be less straightforward than once imagined, some at least have produced essentially Dark Age material, and little or no evidence of use in the pre-Roman Iron Age

(Alcock, 1980). On that basis, for there appear to be no finds known from the Mither Tap, the Bennachie fort may be attributed to the Picts. It is without parallel in the North-East knuckle of Scotland, although a much less well-preserved site, which displays some similar characteristics, has recently been found on Craig Dorney in the Deveron valley.

The remainder of the evidence for Dark Age fortifications in the North-East is drawn from three promontory forts, none of which matches Burghead in scale. Castle Point, Troup, overlooking Cullykhan bay near Pennan, has a long defensive sequence stretching back into the first millennium BC. A vitrified wall, built on a basal layer of timber, reduced the area previously defended, and overlay earlier occupation. It is, however, undated. 'Pictish' occupation is suggested by sherds of late Roman or early medieval date and a fourth century radiocarbon date for a wooden vessel associated with a cobbled floor, which lay outside the vitrified wall, but behind another defensive line of substantially earlier construction (Greig, 1970; 1972).

The evidence for the early use of the sandstone promontory of Dundarg is equally based on partial excavation. Interpretation of the initial phases of use of this site is hampered by the subsequent construction of a castle and a dwelling-house on it and by the lack of diagnostic small finds securely related to the earlier occupation of the promontory. The site's most recent excavators (Fojut and Love, forthcoming) have substantially revised the sequence of constructions on and adjacent to the promontory from that advanced by Simpson (1954; 1960). Two pre-Medieval defensive systems may be represented, both consisting of ramparts and ditches. Of these, the second, noted for the first time by the recent excavators just outside the medieval gatehouse, represents a reduction of the enclosed area and may tentatively be ascribed to the Pictish period. Whilst documentary evidence, in the form of the marginal notes in the Book of Deer, indicates that the *cathair* or fort of 'Abbordobor' (Aberdour) was made over to the Church in the persons of Columba and Drostan, there is no evidence of ecclesiastical activity during this period on the promontory to lend support to the hypothesis that Dundarg was this *cathair*.

If indeed Dundarg was no longer of military significance by this time, the same is not true of the Green Castle, a quartzite promontory jutting seaward on the eastern side of Portknockie harbour. Excavations there have demonstrated that the landward side of this promontory was defended by yet another elaborate variant form of timber-laced wall, in this case involving longitudinal, transversal and vertical oak timbers jointed together. This wall was erected about 700 AD on the basis of radiocarbon dates: in structural terms, its best parallel lies in the much grander fort at South Cadbury, in southern England (Alcock, 1983, fig 1). Behind the Portknockie wall lay plentiful evidence of occupation. Metalworking is attested by mould and crucible fragments and by a bowl furnace. Most of the small finds are not chronologically diagnostic. The likelihood is that the site was already occupied, and defended by a stockade, in the pre-Roman Iron Age, but, given the apparently unchanging character of the main artefact type—pottery—recovered throughout the sequence of deposits on the site, the date of the beginning of the occupation will depend on radiocarbon analyses, presently awaited.

The fact that we are better informed about coastal sites is largely a result of the course of archaeological research in recent years. However, it is perhaps not unreasonable to suggest that the presence of Viking settlements on the other side of the Moray Firth might have occasioned a need for seaward surveillance. All four promontory sites mentioned above occupy prominent headlands strung out along the Moray Firth coast, and all except Dundarg offer some shelter for boats in their immediate vicinity. The subjugation of the Orkneys and other episodes in the historical record make clear the fact that the Picts possessed a navy. There is at least the possibility that some of these promontories (and perhaps others on this coast; Ralston, 1980) served as home ports for such a force.

Furthermore, the quantities of oak wood required in some of their defences is remarkable, and some may have been imported by sea. A record of wood being towed from Northern Scotland to Iona in the early seventh century suggests that this was certainly technically feasible (Anderson, 1922, 188).

Cave sites with evidence of use during our period are equally coastal in location. Examples in the North-East are few in number. Early this century, a jet armlet and some bone pins were found in one west of the harbour at Findochty, but by far the most important example in the Sculptor's Cave near Covesea on the coast of Moray.

This substantial cavern at the foot of sandstone cliffs was excavated by Miss Sylvia Benton over fifty years ago. The parts left unexcavated at that stage have been excavated recently by Ian and Alexandra Shepherd. The location of the cave, and others in its vicinity, makes plain the difficulty of access to them (Ralston, 1983, ill 2).

The more recent excavations have added significantly to our knowledge of this cave's earliest occupation, belonging to the later part of the Bronze Age. However, the examination of undisturbed deposits in the cave's two mouths produced no further finds to add to the collection made by Miss Benton which are attributable to a second period of use in the first millennium AD. This second period assemblage is of particular interest in view of the presence of incised Pictish carvings and simple latin crosses on the walls of the cave. The Shepherds, aided by artificial lighting, have been able to boost the tally of Pictish carvings previously recorded by Allen and Anderson (1903). Although Thomas (1963) has suggested that this cave art at Covesea, and also in a series of caves along the Fife coast near East Wemyss, may represent some of the earliest of Pictish carvings, it is unfortunately impossible securely to relate the second period debris within the Sculptor's Cave with the carving of the symbols.

The interpretation of the character of this second period material has always puzzled commentators, in that it does not appear to represent a normal collection of 'domestic' debris. Indeed Shepherd has suggested that the bulk of the post-Bronze Age material found by Miss Benton may represent a single event—'a hoard of scrap scattered in the cave' (1983, 334). Miss Benton's section drawing (1931, fig 3) illustrates the fact that the later finds came from a layer of very variable thickness which sloped back steeply from the summit of an earlier accumulation at the mouth of the cave. This topmost layer apparently contained 'floors, hardened by fire and trampling' (Benton, 1931, 180), a report which was not confirmed in the more recent, but smaller-scale, excavation.

The first excavation produced a wide range of material, including Roman coins of the 350s and 360s, counterfeit copies of Roman coins, some adapted for use as jewellery, and sherds of samian pottery. A range of metal items was dominated by bronze pins and toilet items, but there were also one or two silver examples. Lead weights or whorls were also found, as well as more prosaic items like glass beads and stone discs. Miss Benton trenchantly observed (1931, 205): 'I do feel rather strongly that none of these articles are really suitable for cave-dwellers'. Whilst the Roman pottery is of second century AD date, the entire assemblage could have been brought to the cave two centuries later. Whatever the circumstance or circumstances that provoked the deposition of this important collection of items, it seems reasonably clear that normal, domestic occupation is not the most likely explanation (Shepherd, 1983).

Elsewhere in Britain, another structural type found increasingly frequently in Dark Age contexts is the timber hall. Such substantial timber buildings may occur in palace complexes, as at Yeavering in Northumberland (Hope-Taylor, 1977) or in more isolated circumstances (Alcock, 1980, 84).

Cropmarks of what appear to be large timber halls were first noted in North-East Scotland in 1976. The example selected for excavation was chosen on the basis of the apparent similarity of its ground-plan and size to those of the earlier of two halls at Doon Hill, near Dunbar in East Lothian (Reynolds, 1978). Since the second hall at Doon Hill shows close stylistic affinities with examples at Yeavering, it may reasonably be dated to *c* 640, when the Anglian take-over of Lothian happened. Thus the first Doon Hill hall should have been built several decades earlier, a date which might also be attributable, by analogy, to the North-East example (Hope-Taylor, 1980). Unfortunately, this hall, at Balbridie Farm, near Crathes, proved to be very much older, and to be attributable to Neolithic settlers (Ralston, 1982).

The result is that it is now impossible, without excavation, to suggest whether cropmarks of other, apparently isolated, halls in the North-East are likely to have been Neolithic or Pictish constructions. Documented Pictish sites have so far failed to produce evidence of similar buildings. One site which gives grounds for optimism is the major Pictish and Scoto-Pictish royal centre at Forteviot, to the south of the River Earn, although the complex of cropmarks noted on this site does not so far include a feasting-hall (Alcock, 1982, fig 14.6). Meantime, the evidence from Balbridie is a salutory example of the dangers of suggesting date on the basis of ground-plan. However, one substantial timber building identified from the air at Monboddo in the Mearns may tentatively be attributed to the Picts. The plan of this example shows some differences from other hall cropmarks in the North-East, including the presence of an entrance in the middle of one of its long sides. Moreover, the building is centrally placed within an oval enclosure (Ralston, 1984,) which may, with reserve, permit comparison with the polygonal stockade which surrounded Doon Hill.

Material culture: a note

The catalogue section, below, details some of the objects made and used by the Picts and their later prehistoric forerunners. Whilst finds have been made at a number of the settlement sites discussed above, a fuller reconsideration of the material culture of the Picts will depend heavily on objects recovered from a series of excavations in 'peripheral' Pictland, in the Orkneys and Hebrides (eg Ritchie, 1977; Crawford, 1977; Hedges and Bell, 1980; Curle, 1982; Hunter, 1984). It would be premature to attempt such a review here, although it is perhaps worth stating that the range of items from the North-East includes both extremes—from accomplished silverwork to everyday domestic pottery.

Amongst the metalwork, the hoard from Gaulcross (no 25) is a testimony to the skill of Pictish silver-smiths. Far to the north, the discovery of a hoard of silver at St Ninian's Isle in the Shetlands led to the recognition of a class of brooches as Pictish products: one, now lost, had previously been found in our area at Banchory (Small *et al* 1973, pl xla). The finer products of Pictish workshops display wide external contacts and influences, as well as considerable technical achievements. In this, they match the art most fully known in stone.

Pictish Art

Pictish art is dominated by the sculptural tradition, though to what extent this represents a real preference of medium, as opposed to better survival possibilities, is not ascertainable. As systematized by Anderson in Anderson and Allen (1903a), this sculpture can be subdivided into three broad classes, whose numerical sequence appears to have been matched, at least broadly, by their date of production. The bulk of this sculpture appears on free-standing stones, although occasionally cave walls and indeed other rock faces were used.

Class I stones are distinguished by the irregularity of the shape of the blocks selected for carving, and by the preferred technique, incision, of the artist-masons. The designs carved on the monoliths offer the principal means of approaching questions of chronology, given the absence of useful archaeological associations and the paucity of inscriptions, and to these symbols we shall subsequently return. It is however pertinent to remark at the outset that the range of designs found on Class I stones lack the overt Christian imagery of the Cross. An exception to this is an incised slab from Raasay, Skye (Curle, 1940, 67 and pl XVIIIc). Certain designs are duplicated, with variations, on small portable objects of bone, stone and metal, but few of these have survived.

Class III stones are dominated by images of the Cross, and are carved in relief. Such Free Crosses and Cross-slabs lack the suites of symbols which serve to characterize the Class I stones. In this restricted sense, there is nothing exclusively 'Pictish' about them. Class II stones form an intermediate group, in terms of their iconography. Like the Class III stones, they are carved in relief, although this was often initially very shallow, at least when the geology of the selected stone permitted. Class II stones consist of prepared, shaped slabs. In terms of the imagery depicted, this class offers an admixture of the Cross and other Christian motifs with the symbols already apparent on Class I stones. Christian and non-Christian imagery usually occupy opposing faces of the stone. It is likely that the dates of production of Classes I and II, and of Classes II and III, overlapped.

The distribution of Class I monuments is heavily weighted in favour of the eastern mainland of Scotland north of the Forth. Isolated examples exist further south, in the Northern Isles, and in the Atlantic West, for example, on Skye. The majority however occur in the area taken here as the North-East, more particularly in the basin of the river Don. Class II stones are distributed rather differently. They are restricted to the eastern mainland, and are rare north of the Dornoch Firth or south of the Tay estuary. The bulk of this series is distributed over the tract of low ground between the Earn and the South Esk in Perthshire and Angus.

It is sometimes suggested that these distributions have chronological significance, but this is not incontrovertible, since the argument turns on absence of evidence. With the exception of a wild boar incised on outcropping bedrock in the stronghold of Dunadd in Argyll, Pictish sculpture is absent in that county. Thus, the argument goes, the development of Class I sculpture must post-date the historically-documented arrival of Scotic settlers from the other side of the North Channel. The Dunadd carving, accompanied by an Ogham inscription, may be conveniently explained away as a witness of the re-assertion of Pictish power in this area in the mid-eighth century, not eradicated by the Scots when they in turn repossessed the site. However, it is by no means certain that the Scots were not infiltrating this area before the historically-attested incursion. Moreover, the pre-existing group in Argyll were known to Ptolemy as the Epidii, a recognisably British name. It is thus possible that there are no Pictish stones in Argyll as that peninsula never formed part of their domain. However, the testimony of Bede, in a passage derived from an earlier source in which he describes the early (mythical) history of the Picts, is against this view.

Contrastingly, an earlier suggestion that Aberdeenshire, with the highest number of Class I stones on a county basis, was the initial centre from which the tradition of carving was to be disseminated, has been overturned on stylistic grounds by Henderson (1958). She has argued in favour of the lowlands around the inner Moray Firth as the origin centre, with the techniques and repertoire of the carving spreading therefrom under the impetus of kingly approval. Suitable candidates suggested for this role include Bridei mac Maelchon, the contemporary of Saint Columba, or Bridei mac Bili, who ruled in the second half of the seventh century (Henderson, 1967, 112). It is perhaps legitimate to question whether the Pictish kingdom was sufficiently centralised for one area, indeed for one individual, to dominate its cultural development.

The chronology of these stones is still subject to considerable dispute. The essential framework is provided by stylistic considerations of the symbols themselves, and comparisons with designs occurring further afield and on other media. R B K Stevenson has championed a late date, well into the seventh century, whereas other authors, notably A C Thomas, have argued for a substantially earlier start. Henderson (1967) may be described as occupying the middle ground, although in terms of both absolute chronology and stylistic influences her viewpoint is considerably closer to Stevenson's than to that of authors who see in this material vestiges of the art of the European pre-Roman Iron Age, and/or Late Antique Art.

The late date—a little before 700—favoured by Stevenson (1955a; 1971; 1976) depends on seeing "the whole system as devised . . . under the influence of the Evangelists' animal symbols and other Christian manuscript sources" (Stevenson, Appendix 2, in re-edition of Wainwright, 1955, 167). The manuscripts in question were illuminated at monasteries such as Iona and Lindisfarne in a style termed Hiberno-Saxon. Thus the Pictish bestiary is indebted to luxury Gospel Books, but the image of the Cross is not taken up in the Pictish area initially. Furthermore, the closest stylistic analogies are not with the earliest of these works, such as the *Book of Durrow*, but with the succeeding generation. The animal heads are best paralleled in the *Lindisfarne Gospels*. An imaginary creature, sometimes called the 'Beast' or the 'Elephant', would owe its long snout and other peculiarities of its physiognamy to an ancestry apparent in the *Book of Durrow*, in the Sutton Hoo hoard, and in subsequent metalwork.

Underpinning the argument for late development is the idea of the 'declining symbol'. This has two implications. The first of these is that there is a 'pure' form of each symbol, from which subsequent deviations represent either simplifications or slightly baroque elaborations. The second implication, rooted in the continued use of the symbols on the Class II stones, is that further chronological subdivision may be possible on these stylistic grounds. Again attributable to Stevenson's consideration of the corpus of Pictish art, this idea was first exemplified with

reference to the Crescent symbol. By definition, the earliest example should contain "a majority of the details found in the others, details which it would have been hard to combine, but which could have separated during simplification" (Stevenson, 1955a, 104). This approach has been extended by Henderson (1958; 1967). However, the equation of typology with chronology cannot be adhered to absolutely, and not all sequences are entirely convincing.

Contrastingly, Henderson (1967) is not prepared to envisage the art of the Pictish stones as wholly derivative, even in those aspects for which parallels can be cited further South. In considering the apparent indebtedness of the animal symbols, she notes that the hound or 'wolf' carved on a slab from Ardross is much more accomplished technically than the lion depicted in the *Book of Durrow*. The latter creature is described as a 'painting of a hard metal jewel' (Henderson, 1967, 123 and figs 23-24) of the type familiar in the Anglo-Saxon world. Thus the differently-depicted animals in the next generation of Northumbrian manuscripts are considered to adopt traits from the Pictish art.

If this is accepted, it frees the chronology of the Pictish bestiary from following manuscript developments, and allows the art style of the incised animals to have begun by 600, and possibly in the latter part of the preceding century. Other authors have suggested yet earlier beginnings for at least some aspects of the Class I art. Curle advocated a late 6th century date for the first inscribed stones on the basis of comparisons with late Celtic metalwork (1940). Two years later, an earlier start date was proposed, and links with Eurasion art styles and other considerations led Thomas, in his review of the evidence (1963), to push for an earlier date, perhaps in the fifth century. Laing and Laing have recently reviewed some evidence for links with the art of the late Antique world, which would again permit a beginning for this art before the 6th century (forthcoming).

In adopting the 'declining symbol' thesis, a case may be made for a symbol stone, re-used as a cist cover at Golspie, Sutherland (Henderson, 1967, 216, no 31) representing the earliest extant stone. Both the Crescent and V-rod, and the 'Beast' symbols are shown in their 'correct' form. Another symbol on this slab, a comb, is single-sided, and invites comparison with that from Fairygreen (no 19). Accepting this idea would add strength to the apparent lateness of the whole tradition, for, since the 'Beast' is often suggested to have been devised in the late 8th century (Curle, 1940, 75: Stevenson, 1955a, 10) the association on the Golspie slab would entail a similarly-late date for the Crescent and V-rod. Thus, the competing chronologies summarily outlined by Stevenson (1959: appendix) are still current.

It may however be noted that, if stylistic decline is the hall-mark of the sequencing of the Class I slabs, the Hiberno-Saxon manuscript tradition with which it is related did not follow a similar course. It should be stated that direct links between monastic scriptoria, producing elegant Gospel books, and Pictish masons, are unproven. Nechtan's request for technical help in the construction of a stone-built church indicates that local masons were unfamiliar with stone architecture as it developed in Northumbria, so that they are most likely to have obtained sight of Hiberno-Saxon designs within Pictland, perhaps in the early monastic foundations. But if other media, embroidery perhaps, or tattooing, offered the link between the two traditions, our reliance on a handful of illustrated texts may well have the affect of depressing the dating of the first sustained series of carved stones in northern Scotland since the cup-marked monuments of the Bronze Age.

The dating of the emergence of Class II sculpture is subject to a broader measure of agreement than is the case for Class I. Appropriate Hiberno-Saxon models, in stone, but more particularly in the luxury illuminated manuscripts, suggest the decades after 700 for traits shared with that tradition. Whilst a substantial portion of Southern Pictland had been under Anglian domination for the half-century prior to 685, an Anglian acquisition which might have made Northumbrian work more readily accessible to Pictish artists, the appearance of a pro-Northumbrian outlook during the reign of Nechtan in the early eighth century may have increased Pictish susceptibility to influences from this direction.

The Class II work is indisputably Christian, and is dated by most authors to the period after the reformation of the Pictish Church, discussed above.

The clearest feature on this class II slab at Migvie, near Tarland, is a cross with complex interlace patterns. Vestigial symbols are faintly visible in the angles between the arms of the cross.

Stevenson's suggestion (1971) of a date towards the middle of the eighth century received a measure of support from Cramp's dating (1978) of the earliest Anglian crosses to about 740. However, there are considerable differences between the two sculptural traditions at this stage, and a more precocious date for early Class II sculpture is advocated by both Curle (1940) and Henderson (1967). Curle suggested that the form of the earliest cross-slabs in Pictland was derived from early Christian monuments in Ireland and in the British kingdoms of southern Scotland (1940, 71-80). Pictish cross-slabs show a wide range of external influences, including Irish and Northumbrian manuscripts and sculpture, as well as traits derived from the Classical world and exotic items from Europe and the Near East. The degree to which the Pictish artists could have had direct access to some of this material, as opposed to being dependent on the art of intermediaries—such as the powerful kingdom of Mercia—is open to dispute.

One of the earliest of the Class II stones on stylistic grounds is that from Aberlemno in Angus. This bears a cross, the central boss of which can be related to Anglo-Saxon metalwork of an early date. Echoes of the *Lindisfarne Gospels* can be seen in the differentiation of the embellishment of the cross-arms from the cross-shaft (Henderson, 1967). The 'snapping' beasts "might have come straight out of the Lindisfarne Gospels" (Stevenson, 1955a, 113). The rear of the stone carries two Pictish symbols and a battle scene, not directly paralleled elsewhere, and perhaps inspired by an European tapestry or wall-painting. All the earliest cross-slabs are to be found in the area south of the Mounth, perhaps partly owing to the relative ease of contact with the Northumbrian area.

The relief tradition in sculpture appears to have become more elaborate through time. An increasing range and number of borrowings mark this sequence. In time, recognisable 'Pictish' elements disappear, although the art of the Class III stones continues to make use of traits already discernable in the Class II tradition. Class II stones of early date are found in the

North-East, but very rarely. One, inscribed with the name PIDARNOIN, stands in the church at Fordoun in the Mearns. Early Class II stones are absent between there and a group from further north, of which the stone from Hilton of Cadboll is the best early example. The modelling of the relief is here much higher than in the early Angus Class II stones. The vine scroll which surrounds the hunting scene on the Cadboll stone is 'inhabited', a tradition derived ultimately from late Classical sources and also found in Anglian work (Henderson, 1978, 1983). A variant of this device recurs later on a most important Class III work, the tall slab called Sueno's Stone at Forres.

The scene carved on the Hilton of Cadboll slab is eclectic in its range of subjects, and is symptomatic of wide Pictish contacts with art traditions further south. Whilst this area, around the inner Moray Firth, continued to display a vigorous sculptural tradition, monuments in earlier Class II style are conspicuous by their absence in the North-East. Only six examples, all of later Class II work, are known in total from this area, and none appears to be earlier than the mid-ninth century. An indication that Class III stones were already being produced perhaps before some Class II works is offered by the design of the cross on a slab at Loch Kinord (Stevenson, 1955a).

The major late Class II monument in the North-East is the Maiden Stone at Chapel of Garioch. The cross on one face is matched by a set of symbols, each in an individual panel, on the other. Further west, the late survival of the Class II tradition is indicated by the Glenferness, Nairn, stone, which combines a cross, in the Northern 'boss' style, with a reverse side displaying a hunting scene and degenerate symbols. Other North-East Class II stones, including those from Dyce, Migvie and Formaston (no 18) display the symbols on the same side as the cross, though in positions subordinate to it. Both the Formaston stone, and another, from Brodie in Moray, bear inscriptions for which a date in the second half of the ninth century is not inappropriate. Thus it is possible that some of the North-East Class II stones post-date the accession of Kenneth mac Alpin, but it is not improbable that such political changes further south had little immediate impact on artistic conventions. Indeed, the reverse might be more surprising.

The most elaborate Class III monuments in the North-East occur in the Laigh of Moray. Sueno's stone is the best-known example, but fragments of other impressive works are known from Kineddar (nos 30, 31). Whilst Irish parallels are often cited for some of their characteristics, other elements may be matched in the later Anglo-Saxon repertory (Henderson, 1978): vine-scroll is a case in point (Henderson, 1983).

In general, sculpture of this late period has been considered to display a decline in quality, a process which Stevenson has referred to as 'barbarisation' (1955a, 125). In part, this appearance may be attributed to the loss of the paint which once covered them, assuming that such works in Pictland were painted as later Northumbrian and Viking-period sculpture appears to have been. Whether this was the case or not, such late works indicate the continuing presence, during these troubled times, of patrons with considerable resources.

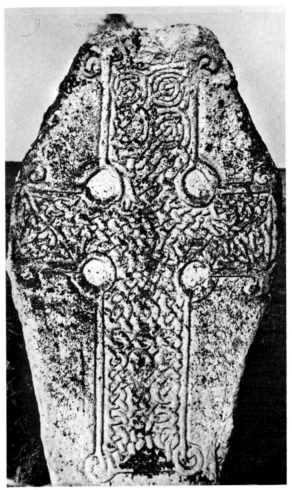

This elaborately carved class III stone at Kinord near Dinnet marks the ultimate development of Pictish sculpture.

Conclusion

This survey has touched on various aspects of the Dark Ages of North-East Scotland, sometimes attempting to illuminate matters by looking rather further afield. It inevitably reflects those parts of Pictish life and society about which we are better informed, and relegates others for which information for our area is as yet in short supply. For example, far more is known about the royal succession than about ordinary family life, but we may suspect that the matrilinear system was defunct for the bulk of the population, at least in Christian times, since Christian authors do not comment upon it.

Fundamental questions concerning the economy need more solid data for reasonable answers to be given (Whittington, 1980), but there seems little reason to doubt that the Picts of the North-East had developed an agrarian economy solidly based on the achievements of their predecessors. The distribution of 'Pit' names is centred on better-quality agricultral areas (Whittington, 1975). Similarly, Edwards' work at sites in the Howe of Cromar indictes both stock-raising and cultivation in that area in the first millennium (1979, fig 1).

Whilst the Picts may have represented nothing more than a terrifying barbarian war-band to Gildas, and indeed to some later writers, there is no doubt that the Pictish state at its most powerful was a considerable, and organised, power. In that sense, the rise of the Scots, representing the extension of the political power of a group initially based on the Atlantic fringe of Scotland, at the expense of one which held the agricultural heartland, is remarkable. That this was achieved when that fringe was itself being subjected to near-constant harrying, is even more surprising. By the time the new aristocracies of Scotland were to petition the Pope about national independence in the Declaration of Arbroath of 1320, memories of the Pictish contribution to the making of Scotland had been suppressed.

Catalogue

1
Stone cup
Culblean Hill, near Dinnet, Aberdeenshire

Stone cups have been found in association with a variety of site types that were in use during the last few centuries BC and the first few AD, including forts, brochs and souterrains. This example was found near, or perhaps within, one of the 'hut-circles'—the dry-stone foundations for round houses—on Culblean Hill. The extensive remains on this hill were described by Ogston (1931, 113-25).

The majority of stone cups have been found in North-East Scotland (Steer, 1956, 243-6): there is a particular concentration of examples known from the Howe of Alford. They are likely to have been used as lamps, although there is considerable variation in the proportions of the bowls, and some may have served as cups or mortars.

This particular example is unusual in being made of granite and in the high quality of its finish.

Purchased from the 'museum' at the Burn o' Vat (just below Culblean) by Dr Johnson before 1920, and gifted by his widow, Dr Esther Johnson, to the Museum, Marischal College, in 1964.

Height 74mm: diameter 75mm

Catalogue number: ABDUA 17413

Unpublished

2
Stone cup
Aberdeenshire, no precise location

Approximately half of the stone cups from North-East Scotland show evidence of decoration. More than half are made of steatite or soapstone. This steatite cup may be considered to display 'typical' features, including a perforated handle and a simple herringbone design incised around its handle and rim.

In the early 19th century they were fancifully described as 'druidical paterae', but a range of more prosaic functions is likely.

Steer, K A 1956, 243-6

Height 60.5mm: diameter 105mm

Catalogue number: ABDUA 17423

Unpublished

3
Stone cup
Wester Clova, Kildrummy, Aberdeenshire

This handle-less sandstone cup or mortar was found within the complex of souterrains which abound in the area around Wester Clova. Other stone cups have been found in a monument of this type at Migvie.

This cup is smaller than most of the series, and may have served for grinding pigments or other substances. On the assumption that it was made when the souterrains were in use, it may be ascribed tentatively to the first few centuries AD.

Michie, J 1887, no 0-21
Reid, R W 1912, no I-132

Found and presented to the Museum, University of Aberdeen, in 1886, by the Reverend Professor J Christie.

Height 66 mm: diameter 63.5 mm
Catalogue number: ABDUA 17410

4
Long-handled stone cup or ladle
Woodside Croft, Hill of Skares, Culsalmond, Aberdeenshire

Such objects appear to be comparatively rare discoveries, and may have had wooden prototypes, such as the ladle from Lochlee Crannog, Ayrshire. Although found loosely associated with two other cups of more usual form in material removed from a cairn, this undecorated steatite example, with its long handle perforated at the end, may have served a different purpose. Traditionally such objects are attributed to the first couple of centuries AD, but a wider date range is possible.

Glaister, J 1911, vol 2, 861, no 14
Callander, J G 1916
Simpson, W D 1943, 51 and Pl 29

Whilst the two other stone cups, one of which was decorated (Callander, 1916, 146 and fig 1) were recovered when the cairn was dismantled, the ladle was recovered subsequently amongst material removed to

Colpy. The ladle was bequeathed by Dr J Graham Callander to the Museum, Marischal College in 1938. The decorated cup is in the National Museum of Antiquities in Edinburgh.

Height 63 mm: diameter 70 mm
Catalogue number: ABDUA 17409

5
Stone cup
Dunnideer, Insch, Aberdeenshire

This steatite cup or lamp was found within the later prehistoric fort on Dunnideer Hill, near Insch. This site shows superficial traces of a long and complex history of settlement use, possibly beginning early in the first millennium BC. It is thus impossible securely to date the cup by its association with the fort, although the fact that it was recovered within the virtified enclosure which crowns the hill allows the possibility that this example may date relatively early in the sequence.

At least three other stone cups or lamps have been found in Scottish vitrified forts, which, given the early radiocarbon dates that have been furnished by some of these, provides some support for the idea (Callander, 1916; Childe, 1935, 246-7), then couched in rather different terms, that this type of object may already have been in use in the Bronze Age. Production of items of this type is indicated at Dunagoil on Bute, but they are likely to have been made at many places.

Steer, K A 1956, 243-6
Bequeathed by Dr W Douglas Simpson to the Museum, Marischal College, in 1968.
Height 60mm: diameter 70mm
Catalogue number: ABDUA 17408
Unpublished

6
Stone cup
Mill of Syde, Kennethmont, Aberdeenshire

This irregularly-decorated stone cup was found, within the angle of 'two buried walls' in a garden. The incised decoration is fairly crude. The handle of the cup lacks a perforation, but displays an incised rectangle on its upper surface. It may have been used as a lamp, and was probably made around the early centuries AD.

Steer, K A 1956, 243-6
Found while gardening near a 'buried construction' in 1980. On loan from Mr Catto, Kennethmont.
Height 70mm: diameter 104mm
Catalogue number: ABDUA 17810
Unpublished

7
Pottery
Culbin Sands, Moray

In comparison with some areas of Britain, the quantity of pottery from North-East Scotland datable to the last millennium BC and the first millennium AD is not large. Apart from products imported from the Roman world, little can presently be said about the date of manufacture of particular vessels, devoid of their context, over this long period. However, recent excavations, particularly on promontory forts, have produced more substantial quantities of this material, and the essence of a local sequence, at least for the South coast of the Moray Firth, should be forthcoming.

The pots from which these fragments survive were made without the use of the potter's wheel, which was known further south in Britain at the end of the first millennium BC. They were probably fired in temporary kilns, often called 'pit clamps', or even on bonfires.

These sherds all come from domestic pottery, probably made locally. The rim sherds from a large vessel suggest its former use—for storage.

These sherds were all collected in the Culbin Sands before 1930, and were bequeathed to the Museum, Marischal College, by Dr J G Callander in 1938.

The large storage vessel was some 315mm in diameter.

Catalogue numbers: ABDUA 15657 and 15658
Unpublished

8
Bronze snake armlet
Culbin Sands, Moray

This unique item, a two-headed snake with three coils, incorporates a longstanding favourite motif of Celtic craftsmen—the use of animal designs. Another snake armlet, considered to have been ancestral to the Scottish series, was found at Snailwell in Cambridgeshire.

The two mouths would originally have held a coloured stud, probably of enamel or glass: the pupils of the eyes are of blue glass. Details of the cast bronzework, more especially the 'slender trumpets' or 'broken-backed spirals', which delineate the eyes, are a recurrent motif in late British Iron Age art, and may be paralleled for example on the war-trumpet from Liecheston Farm, Deskford, Banffshire.

Bronze working flourished in North Britain in the first two or three centuries AD. Much of the work in this style was concentrated in the North-East of Scotland, and this item has been considered to be ancestral typologically to one of the main series produced here—the massive armlets (see no 9). This snake armlet is likely to have been made in the first or second centuries AD.

As well as appearing in rather different guise on Pictish stones, the use of a snake as a decorative element may be paralleled on a much smaller bracelet from Hurly Hawkin broch, Angus (MacGregor, 1976 no 216) and, incised on a steatite cup, from Newton of Auchingool, Inverkeithny, Banffshire (Thomas, 1961, 38 and pl 1 lower; MacGregor, 1976, no 334).

Stevenson, R B K 1966, 32 and pl 5a
Simpson, M 1968, 243 and fig 62
Megaw, J V S 1970, no 302
Piggott, S 1970, no 136
MacGregor, M 1976, no 214
Clarke, D V and Ralston, I B M 1978, no 33

Found in 1823 or 1824 amongst sand dunes on the W side of the River Findhorn by a sportsman and sold to a local shopkeeper. In the possession of Lady Gordon Cumming of Altyre in 1881, it was subsequently purchased by the National Museum in 1930.

Diameters: maximum 89mm; internal 64mm

On loan from the National Museum of Antiquities of Scotland

Catalogue number: FA89

9
Bronze penannular armlet
Links of Drumside, Belhelvie, Aberdeenshire

Oval cast bronze armlets of this 'massive' type are thought to have been derived from the 'snake' type (see

no): in these later examples, the snake has been stylised to such an extent that its reptilian origins are unrecognisable.

The large voids in the terminals were intended to hold enamel plates (which survive in other examples), as is shown by the disposition of a pair of rivets, with countersunk heads, adjoining each hole.

The descriptions of 'heavy' or 'massive' that are frequently applied to bronzework of this type are apposite: this example weighs approximately 11lb 12oz. Some may have been worn round the leg rather than the arm. Production in North-East Scotland and during the period 100-300 AD may be considered likely: the cast bronze decoration has been considered to incorporate design elements borrowed from Ireland (Kilbride-Jones, 1980), as well as from further south within Britain. Provincial Roman influence—in the use of enamel—is also recognisable.

At two sites in the North-East, such armlets are associated, albeit loosely, with souterrains. At Castle Newe in Strathdon, a first century AD Roman coin was also found. Three armlets found near Crossford, Coull, apparently came from within an 'enclosure', near which were two souterrains.

Smith, J A 1881b, 333-5 and figs 14-15
Stevenson, R B K 1966, 31-2
Simpson, M 1968, 233-54 and fig 58a
MacGregor, M 1976, no 236
Kilbride-Jones, H E 1980, 153-4

Found at a depth of 6 feet and subsequently presented to the National Museum of Antiquities of Scotland by John Stuart in 1853 (*Proc Soc Antiq Scot*, 1, 1851-4, 138). Another example, now lost, was found about three yards away.

Diameter: (maximum) 92.5mm

On loan from the National Museum of Antiquities of Scotland

Catalogue number: FA 16

10
Miniature cast bronze cauldron, silver brooch and 'playing-pieces'
Waulkmill, near Tarland, Aberdeenshire

A number of discoveries appear to have been made in this sandpit, beside a demolished stone circle, at the end of last century (Coles, 1905). Unfortunately, the standard of recording was not high, so that associations between objects—essential both for dating and in assessing their significance—are now uncertain. Furthermore, material found in 1899, later than the items discussed here, is only known by hear-say. However, further silver items appear to have been unearthed (Coles, 1905, 215). Whilst Coles talks of a 'stone coffin', and later authors, following Callander, mention a deposit of bones (which crumbled to dust) under a 'nest of stones' (Simpson, 1943, 76—for whom the bones represented a cremation), it is by no means certain that the following material formed a single assemblage, deposited at the same time.

The bronze cauldron was found loosely associated with an inhumation burial, represented solely by the crown of a single molar. Other gravegoods consisted of about twenty glass and stone 'playing-pieces' and a silver penannular brooch of Fowler type Aa: this type is usually considered to date to the first two centuries AD, but the use of silver would permit a considerably later date. It thus does not assist in the dating of the cauldron, and it is possible that material was buried at Waulkmill over a lengthy period.

The cauldron is a diminutive version of the massive sheet-bronze vessels, which were in use from about 700 BC. It is decorated with a beaded carination. The rivets, inserted into pre-drilled holes, have no functional purpose in this small version, although they did in the larger prototypes. In terms of shape, the cauldron is more akin to the Santon series, with projecting bellies, than the globular or Battersea type, also found in the British pre-Roman Iron Age. Nonetheless, the everted neck of the Waulkmill example is exceptional. The Santon type appears to be based on

a European form, in use from about 100 BC, and is found in both Britain and Ireland (Raftery, 1980).

Amongst this series, the closest parallel geographically comes from Carlingwark Loch in the Stewartry of Kirkcudbright, which contained Roman and other material from the decades around 100 AD. It is thus likely that the date of manufacture for the miniature cauldron may lie in the first two centuries AD. A further miniature cauldron has been found associated with Roman material in a pit at Ancaster, Lincolnshire (Robertson, 1970, Table VII).

Other material, recovered at the same time, includes two or three pieces of iron.

Coles, F R 1905
Glaister, J 1911, vol 2, 873
Callander, J G 1915
Curle, J 1932
Hawkes, C F C 1951
Robertson, A 1970, Table VII
MacGregor, M 1976, no 299 (noted as being lost)
Whimster, R 1981

Discovered in 1899, the cauldron was purchased c 1908 from the executors of Inspector Tom Esson, and was bequeathed to the University Museum in 1938 by Dr J Graham Callander. In 1978 it underwent major conservation.

Cauldron: height 39mm; rim diameter 54mm:
ABDUA glass disc: diameter 20.5 mm
Catalogue numbers: cauldron, ABDUA 15643:
blue glass disc ABDUA 15529

All items, apart from the cauldron and one glass disc, *On loan from the National Museum of Antiquities of Scotland*

Catalogue numbers: EQ 278-83: six quartzite discs
EQ 284-6: two blue glass discs and a fragment
EQ 277-8: variegated glass disc and a fragment
EQ 279: silver penannular brooch
EQ 280: cylindrical piece of near-colourless glass

40

11
Glass ball
Jericho, Culsalmond, Aberdeenshire

The glass of this small ball is greenish-blue in colour, similar to that used for Roman bottle glass. The ball exhibits little sign of wear, except where a small portion is chipped. It is decorated with ten spiral designs, laid on and polished flat: seven of these 'eyes' are blue against a pale-blue, almost white, ground, whereas the remaining three are red against a yellow ground.

The function of such glass balls is uncertain. They may have served as 'gaming pieces', as is suggested by the recovery of a set of 24 broadly similar beads (their 'eyes' are formed of interlocked curves) from a rich burial at Welwyn Garden City, Hertfordshire, dated to about 10 BC (Stead, 1967, 14-19 and fig 10). Stead (1967, 19) discusses the types of games which may have been played.

Scottish comparanda are known from the major hill-fort of Traprain Law, East Lothian, and from a broch

site at the Hurly Hawkin in Angus. Two examples, of ice-green glass with blue and white spirals, were included in a hoard of 'charms' deposited in an empty cist in a ring cairn at Monquhitter, Aberdeenshire (Anderson, 1902; Stevenson, 1967). Associated Roman material, where this is helpful in suggesting a date, is broadly of the third century AD.

Anderson, J 1902, 675-88
Glaister, J 1911, vol 2, 873, no 18
Stead, I 1967
Stevenson, R B K 1967
Clarke, D V and Ralston, I B M 1978, no 36
Taylor, D B 1982, 231-2

Discovered before 1910: bequeathed to the University Museum in 1938 by Dr J Graham Callander.

Diameter: 14mm

Catalogue number: ABDUA 15505

Unpublished

12
Rein-ring
Shellagreen (or Sheelagreen), Culsalmond, Aberdeenshire

This example of a 'massive' or 'Donside' terret displays the heaviness which typifies much of the cast bronzework of Caledonian smiths in the early centuries AD. Whilst the type is usually suggested to have been in use before 300 AD, it has been argued that some may have been produced at a later date, for example at Dinas Emrys in North Wales (Alcock, 1963, 69 and 177). A similar terret, from an Anglo-Saxon cemetery (B) at Linton Heath, Cambridgeshire, is likely to have been buried in the fifth century AD (Laing, pers comm).

This terret or rein-ring is distinctly elliptical in shape. Noteworthy are the holes, cut in the bronze symmetrical to the vertical axis of the ring, for the attachment of a decorative embellishment. One of

East. They are thus usually accepted as the products of local craftsmen, and are referred to as 'massive' or 'Donside' terrets. Such horsegear is a recurrent type of find, and may be dated to the first three centuries AD, although others have argued for a later *floruit* for the type (see no 12).

This particular example is smaller than is usual for such terrets. It has also been considered to be a rather

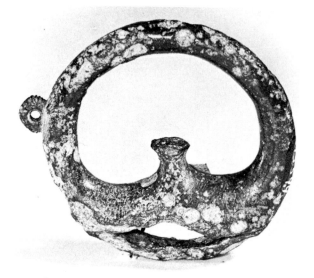

these is approximately circular, whilst the other is diamond-shaped (cf illustration in MacGregor).

Callander, J G 1906, 33-5 and figs 9-10
Glaister, J 1911, vol 2, 862, no 5
Callander J G 1927, 246
Kilbride-Jones, H E 1935, 451-3 and 449, figs 2, 3
Stevenson, R B K 1966
MacGregor, M 1976, no 118 (noted as being lost)
Kilbride-Jones, H E 1980, 155-7

This stray find, discovered before 1885, was in Callander's collection by 1905: it was bequeathed to the University Museum by Dr J Graham Callander in 1938.

Diameter: 86.5mm

Catalogue number: ABDUA 15597

13
Cast bronze rein-ring
'Near the foot of Tap o' Noth', Rhynie, Aberdeenshire

The distribution of developed forms of this type of rein-ring or terret shows a concentration in the North-

unsatisfactory piece of design, as it would have been impossible for the terret to sit firmly on the harness: for this reason, this terret has been suggested as a prototype for the Donside series, in which Piggott (1955, 63) has envisaged influences from Roman military examples: MacGregor (1976, 48) also accepted Continental inspiration for this type. The Rhynie terret is unusual in that it has an additional ring, projecting outwards, probably added for the suspension of an ornament. It is a stray find, but its findspot may not be unconnected with the massive fort on Tap o' Noth.

Whilst the Pictish stones display plentiful evidence of horsemanship, appropriate metal horsegear appears to be rare in the North-East after the Donside terrets.

A swivel-ring from Fortrie of Balnoon, Banffshire (Laing, 1974, 190) may be an exception to this rule.

Kilbride-Jones, H E 1935, 445-54
Stevenson, R B K 1966
McGregor, M 1976, no 123
Kilbride-Jones, H E 1980, 154-7 and fig 43.1

Found before 1935: purchased from Mr A Shand, Longcroft, Rhynie, by Mr G Davidson and presented by him to the University Museum.

Diameter: 50mm

Catalogue number: ABDUA 15599

14
Glass and paste beads
Various localities in Aberdeenshire and Moray

(a) Meare spiral: Culbin Sands, Moray
(b) Meare spiral: Scotston, Insch, Aberdeenshire
(c) Blue annular: Culbin Sands, Moray
(d) Blue annular: Culbin Sands, Moray
(e) Meare spiral on yellow ground: Mill of Gellan, Tarland burn, Tarland, Aberdeenshire
(f) Meare spiral on green ground: Unknown locality, Aberdeenshire

By the early centuries AD, glass beads were known in considerable variety in North Britain. They were produced for the most part by reworking scrap Roman glass. The 'Iron Age' examples here were the forerunners of later fashions. A date range between the last century BC and the first two centuries AD may tentatively be ascribed to them, although some might be as early as the third century BC, and a wide date range is possible for the blue annular beads.

Meare spirals (Guido, 1978, Class 10) are usually translucent and colourless, and are often globular in shape. Their name comes from the Iron Age village in SW England, where some may have been produced. Another Meare spiral from the Culbin Sands, now in the National Museum of Antiquities in Edinburgh, was found fused with part of an armlet of natural greenish glass with coloured cables.

All the examples displayed are stray finds, devoid of useful archaeological contexts.

Laing, L 1975
Guido, M 1978, 79-81 and 187-9

All were discovered before 1915, except (e): (a)-(d) were bequeathed to the University Museum by Dr J Graham Callander in 1938: (e) was presented by Mr A Skene in 1951.

Diameters: (a) 16mm (b) 19mm (c) 7mm
          (d) 4.5mm (e) 17mm (f) 17mm

Catalogue numbers: all ABDUA (a) 15514
                            (b) 15515
                            (c) 15524
                            (d) 15525
                            (e) 15544
                            (f) 15545

Unpublished

15
Glass beads
Aberdeenshire

(a) Banff, Banffshire
(b) Chapel of Garioch, Aberdeenshire
(c) Ballater, Aberdeenshire
(d) Unknown location, Aberdeenshire
(e) Mill of Gellan (= Tarland Burn), Tarland, Aberdeenshire
(f) Kildrummy, Aberdeenshire
(g) Kildrummy, Aberdeenshire
(h) Dukeston, Kildrummy, Aberdeenshire: found in a cist, part of a necklace

These annular beads are normally described as 'North Scottish Annular Beads' (Guido, 1978, Class 14) as the majority of finds have been made in North-East Scotland. They are characterised by what is taken to be a northern predilection for strarkly contrasting colours, usually incorporating yellow decoration. Whilst the place of their manufacture is uncertain, it is sometimes suggested that the craftsmen may have been based in the Culbin area on the south side of the Moray Firth. A plentiful supply of the requisite fine sand would have been available there. Impurities in this raw material may have given rise to the dark colours usually found. A date range centred on the first couple of centuries AD may be suggested for their production, although finds from broch sites in western Scotland might permit earlier beginnings.

All are stray finds, except for the bead from a cist at Dukeston Farm, which lies east of the Don at Kildrummy. Little is known of this late Victorian discovery. Either deposition in an earlier, Bronze Age, cist or an Iron Age burial, from which only the gravegoods survive, is possible.

Michie, J 1887, 11-13
Glaister, J 1911, vol 2, 863, no 3
Reid, R W 1912, no I-382
Guido, M 1978, 87-9 and 197-200

(a)-(d) were in the collection of Dr J G Callander by 1911, and were bequeathed by him to the Museum, Marischal College in 1938. (e) was gifted to the Museum by Mr A Skene in 1951. (f)-(h) were donated to the Museum in 1886 by Reverend Professor J Christie.

Diameters: (a) 22.5mm (b) 25.5mm (c) 22mm (d) 20.5mm (e) 24.5mm (f) 22.5mm (g) 27mm (h) 26mm

Catalogue numbers: all ABDUA (a) 15526
(b) 15530
(c) 15528
(d) 15520
(e) 15539
(f) 15536
(g) 15537
(h) 15538

Part unpublished

16
Jet Objects
from Moray and Aberdeenshire

(a) Ring from Culbin Sands, Moray

(b) Ring from Culbin Sands, Moray

(c) Lenticular bead from Home Farm, Straloch, Newmachar, Aberdeenshire

(d) Pendant from Chapelton, Leslie, Aberdeenshire

Jet and shale, or 'cannel coal' was used intermittently from the Bronze Age for the making of both decorative and functional objects (Shepherd, 1981). Its sources within Britain are for the most part near coal measures, with the jet from Whitby in Yorkshire being particularly prized on account of its quality. In later prehistory, 'semi-industrial' workshops became established in southern Britain for the winning and working of this material (Cunliffe, 1978).

Whilst the dating of such stray finds is not easy, a date range in the early centuries AD for these items is not improbable. Small quantities of jet objects are known from a number of Dark Age sites, including, for example, the Brough of Birsay (Curle, 1982, 67, ill 42).

Length or diameter: (a) 36.5mm (b) 47mm
                    (c) 30mm (d) 55mm

(a) and (b) were once part of the collection of the Reverend John McEwan at Dyke in Moray, and were purchased by Dr J G Callender c 1915. (c) and (d) were in Callander's collection by the same date. All were bequeathed by him to the Museum, Marischal College, in 1938.

Catalogue numbers: all ABDUA (a) 17490
                              (b) 19351
                              (c) 17495
                              (d) 17494

Unpublished

17
Wave-decorated glass beads
Aberdeenshire

(a) Colpy Farm, Culsalmond, Aberdeenshire
(b) Buchan
(c-d) No precise location, Aberdeenshire

Blue annular glass beads with an opaque white wavy decoration seem to have been such a long-lasting element of material culture in Britain during the last centuries BC and the first centuries AD as to merit the epithet 'traditional'. Beads with wavy decoration were being used in Yorkshire from the third century BC at

least. As a rule of thumb, Guido suggests that the later beads in the series are marked by the use of a darker blue glass, by their larger average size, and by the greater irregularity in the wave designs.

Similar beads have been recovered from the Sculptor's Cave at Covesea on the Moray coast (Benton, 1931). Manufacture in the early centuries AD may therefore be considered likely.

Glaister, J 1911, vol 2, 863, no 3
Guido, M 1978, 62-4

All were in the collection of Dr J G Callander by 1915 and were bequeathed by him to the Anthropological Museum in 1938.

Diameters: (a) 33mm (b) 18mm (c) 20mm (d) 17mm
Catalogue numbers: all ABDUA (a) 15506
                                (b) 15531
                                (c) 15532
                                (d) 15533

Unpublished

18
Cross-shaft fragment, Class II
Saint Adamnan's kirkyard, Formaston, near Aboyne, Aberdeenshire

This granite block is a portion of a Class II slab, and is decorated with the mirror symbol in addition to part of the shaft of a cross. Moreover, the stone carries an inscription in the Ogham alphabet. This form of Ogham, termed 'scholastic', was more widely employed in the Irish and Scotic world in the West, whence it was probably introduced to the Picts. Scholastic Oghams date to c 700 at the earliest. The style of the interlaced pattern on the cross-shaft suggest that this slab dates to the very end of the period of Pictish independence in the middle of the ninth century.

It is one of the very few Pictish stones from the core of the North-East to bear a cross. This small series includes the large monolith of the Maiden Stone at Chapel of Garioch, and an example from the vicinity

of Loch Kinord. This last, a Class III stone, bears no symbols, but its cross has many similarities to Formaston, supporting the late date for the Formaston work (Henderson, 1972).

Pictish Ogham inscriptions, like the Pictish language itself, are generally untranslatable at present, although certain elements, such as MAQQ, have been taken as cognates of Irish Celtic words (Jackson, 1955, 140-2). This may mean 'descendant of'. This word occurs on at least four apparently late slabs, and may perhaps be indicative of the decline of matriarchal power amongst the Picts. Both lines read upwards and the full inscription reads:

MAQQ OI TALLUORRH
NAHHTVR OBBACCAANNEVV

If the lines are read from right to left, the order given above would be reversed.

There are indications that the inscription is an afterthought, in so far as one line is carved onto the beading which edges the stone.

Anderson, J and Allen, J R 1903c, 188-9
Simpson, W D 1943, 101-3 and plate 58
Diack, F C 1944, 65-6 and Ill 1
Stevenson, R B K 1955a
Jackson, K 1955

Found in the late 19th century in the churchyard.

Height 1124mm: width 443mm

On loan from the North-East of Scotland Libraries Service Museums Service

Catalogue number: I 6904

19
Symbol stone, Class I
Fairygreen, Collace, Perthshire

This almost-complete slab of finely metamorphised sandstone has been carved with three symbols on a prepared face. The designs used are the mirror-and-comb, the decorated rectangle, and a fine 'Pictish beast'. Whilst most of the faunal symbols on Pictish

creature on the available surface. Present thought would tend to place symbol stones of Class I like this in the period 650-750. The underlying theory includes the assumption that the 'beast' is a late symbol, derived from metalwork or manuscripts, but it has been recently suggested that this creature may derive from late Roman sources. If this is accepted, a date in the sixth century or earlier may be advanced.

When found, the stone was lying face-down, buried in a field. It was not associated with any other material.

Small, A 1962, 221-2

Angus-Butterworth, L M 1967, 55

Discovered in c 1948, the stone was not recognised as an antiquity until 1962. It was presented to the Anthropological Museum by Mr Alexander, *per* Mr Alan Small, in the latter year.

Height 600mm: width 400mm

Catalogue number: ABDUA 15591

20
Symbol stone, Class I
Dinnacaer, near Stonehaven, Kincardineshire

This Old Red Sandstone conglomerate symbol stone is unusual in that it has been decorated on both principal faces. One face displays an incised double disc and z-rod symbol; the other is carved with the 'flower' and mirror-and-comb symbols. It is one of a number of sculptured stones which were found in an 'enclosure' atop what is now an isolated rock stack on the south side of Strathlethan bay, not far from the probable Pictish fort at Dunnottar.

The stones from Dinnacaer are the only Class I stones known from Kincardineshire south of the Mounth, with the possible exception of the almost-illegible Auquhollie Stone at Fetteresso. The coastal location of the Dinnacaer stones is unusual in the North-East.

It is possible to argue for an early date, perhaps in the 5th century, for this stone on stylistic grounds,

stones represent contemporary inhabitants of Scotland, the 'beast' is an exception to the rule. The mirror is of the form normally recorded on Pictish stones, and is similar in shape to Iron Age mirrors of the first and second centuries AD. The single-sided comb, with opposing terminals, may be dated to the fourth or fifth centuries.

The sculptor has had to erase the original line selected for the rear leg of the beast and re-incise it at a lower angle in order to accommodate the entire

the former's property at Banchory House. In 1983 the stone was gifted by the present owners of Banchory House, the Camphill Trust, to the Museum, Marischal College.

Height 640mm: width 380mm

Catalogue number: ABDUA 17862

21
Symbol stone fragment, Class I
Dead Man's Howe, Wantonwells, Insch, Aberdeenshire

This granite slab, buried face down and recovered during ploughing, probably formed the lower part of a larger monumental stone. The surviving incised symbol is the double disc and z-rod. This particular variant (note the radial lines) is similar to, although less elaborate than, another from Dunnichen, Angus, as well as other stones taken to be stylistically late within the Class I monuments. On that basis, the stone may have been carved between 650 and 750. However, a possible parallel between this design and that of saucer brooches, a type of Anglo-Saxon jewellery

although the weight of opinion would subscribe to a date about 200 years later.

Stuart, J 1867, pl XV, no 2

Anderson, J and Allen, J R 1903c, 201, no 4

Simpson, W D 1971

Discovered in 1819, this stone was subsequently built into the wall of a fisherman's house at Stonehaven. In 1858, it was obtained by Alexander Thomson from James Brown, and was built into a garden feature in

(Morris, 1973, 571), would permit a date in the sixth or earlier seventh centuries for the carving of this stone.

Dead Man's Howe, near Insch, nestles in the valley between the Hill of Christ's Kirk, crowned by a palisaded enclosure, and the complex hill-fort on Dunnideer.

Discovery and Excavation in Scotland, 1983, 11
Inglis and Inglis, forthcoming
Found whilst ploughing to a depth of 30cm at NJ 61552745 by Mr Norman Stronach and presented by him to the Museum, Marischal College, in 1983.

Height 1160mm: width 780mm

Catalogue number: ABDUA 15594

22
Symbol stone, Class I
Burghead, Moray

The promontory of Burghead, like that on the Kincardineshire coast at Dunnottar, appears to have been occupied by a major defended site in Pictish times. Subsequent developments at both sites, and spasmodic small-scale excavations, mean that our comprehension of the archaeological sequence on both headlands is limited, but Burghead has produced an important series of Class I incised slabs, and was certainly enclosed by an elaborate timber-laced defence in the first millennium AD.

This is one of six bull slabs recovered from Burghead to have survived, more than twenty further stones having been used in early 19th century coastal works. Incised depictions of this animal are rare elsewhere in the Pictish world, allowing the suggestion that the bull may have been a totemic emblem for the Picts who lived at the site or in its vicinity.

All the surviving Burghead stones are carved on waterworn sandstone boulders, which have been minimally dressed on their sculpted faces. The quality of the carving may be taken as an indication of a date

late in the seventh century for the incision of these slabs, which may have been sculpted little before the transition to Class II. However, an earlier date is not precluded, particularly if the indebtedness of the Pictish animals to manuscript prototypes is rejected.

Mitchell, A 1884, 663-5 & fig 26
Anderson, J and Allen, J R 1903c, 122 (= Burghead 4)
Stevenson, R B K 1955a
Gordon, C A 1966, 218-9
Henderson, I 1967

This slab was found in 1867 whilst 'demolishing an old house on the south quay', and was subsequently held at the Harbourmaster's Office by Mr H W Young.

Dimensions: 280mm × 280mm

On loan from Moray Museums Service

Catalogue number: 1896-6a

23

Symbol stone, Class I
Newbigging, Leslie, Aberdeenshire

Three symbols decorate this slab. The mirror-and-comb and decorated rectangles belong to the abstract tradition. The wolf—a creature not frequently depicted—belongs to the animal series. Animal designs, sometimes stylised, sometimes naturalistically depicted, are a recurrent tradition in European art in later prehistory and during the Dark Ages. The range of possible parallels is therefore wide, and the selection of apposite examples is a dominant strand in providing the chronology for Class I. Naturalistic representation, as here, may belong to either the late 7th century or the earlier part of the 8th, on the basis of parallels with manuscripts, for which the stylistically-similar Ardross slab, now in Inverness Museum, is important. However, both the mirror type, and the comb, the latter of Frisian ancestry and there datable to about the fifth century, would not exclude an earlier, perhaps 6th century, date. The quality of the carving is high in relation to that usually seen on granite slabs.

Stuart, J 1867, pl CXXIII
Anderson, J and Allen, J R 1903c, 177-8
Found in about 1842 while breaking in new ground and subsequently built into a dyke. Later transferred to the farmhouse garden. Presented to the National Trust for Scotland (Leith Hall) in 1905.

Height 635mm: width 380mm

On loan from the National Trust for Scotland

24

Symbol Stone, Class I
Hillhead of Clatt (= Percylieu), Clatt,
Aberdeenshire

This whinstone slab bears a decorated version of the arc symbol and the lower portion of the fish symbol. When found in the first half of last century, the stone was complete, but it was trimmed to make a paving slab for a byre. Typological considerations presently favour the late seventh century for the production of this slab: the fish (salmon?) symbol, in common with most of the animal depictions, is not believed to have been in use before this time (Stevenson, 1955a). The underpinning of this hypothesis depends on relations with the Gospel Books, so that an earlier date is not precluded.

This stone can be loosely associated with a number of structures previously located on the same hill. These included small cairns or clearance heaps, a number of burials (both crouched and extended inhumations in cists), a stone circle, and what may have been a souterrain. At least some of these may have been contemporary with the incised slab, which was found in what was described as a 'paved structure'.

Stuart, J 1856, pl V
Gurnell, J 1884
Anderson, J and Allen, J R 1903c, 181-2
Height 920mm: width 450mm

Found at a depth of 6 feet, whilst trenching close to NJ 565267 before 1840. By 1844 it had been trimmed and was in use as a paving slab. The stone was subsequently moved to Cransmill, near Tap o' Noth, before being donated to the National Trust for Scotland, at Leith Hall, where it has been since 1905.

On loan from the National Trust for Scotland

25

Silver pin, bracelet and chain
Gaulcross, near Fordyce, Banffshire

These three items are all that remain of a much larger hoard, which included a number of brooches as well as further pins. The hoard was deposited inside a much earlier monument—a ring cairn within a stone circle. Hoards are of particular significance in that, whilst not all the objects in them need be of the same date, they must all have been in use at the time of deposit. It has been suggested that this hoard was deposited in the first half of the ninth century, by which time some of the objects were probably already old.

The pin (A) is of a well-known type, known as 'hand-pins', and usually ascribed to about the 7th century (Stevenson, 1955b). The name is derived from a trait seen on some of the series, in which the top part of the head projects forward, in a manner reminiscent of the fingers of a half-closed hand. Part of their background may be seen in pins from Covesea and Traprain Law (Burley, 1956, 169-71). Hand-pins are more commonly found in Ireland. The rear of the Gaulcross pin is decorated with punched dot decoration, while the front of the palm displays triple triscelles and trumpet scrolls. A comparable pin, found at Norrie's Law in Fife, has a Pictish symbol on the rear face: a date in the 6th century has been advanced for this (Fowler, 1963: Thomas, 1963), but has not been universally supported. Whilst the latest coins certainly associated with the Norrie's Law hoard may be late Roman issues, Stevenson (1976) has made out a case for the decoration on the decorated Norrie's Law pin belonging to the 8th century.

The bracelet (B) is formed of a beaten convex strip of silver and may be a 'revival' of the early coil 'bracelets' which are visible on some symbol stones, such as at Keiss, Caithness. This may permit a date in the late 7th, or early 8th, century for manufacture, if a 'high' dating for the stones is preferred.

The chain (C) is unlike the group of Pictish chains, in that it is formed by a series of 'knitted' rings. This trait is shared with some chains in Viking hoards, datable to the 11th century, and also with the much earlier (c 1st century BC) gold chain from Broighter in Ireland. A silver chain from Croy, Inverness-shire, buried about 850, differs from the Gaulcross example, in that, whilst both are knitted, the former is flat and the latter round.

Stuart, J 1856
Anderson, J and Allen, J R 1903
Stevenson, R B K 1955b
Burley, E 1956
Fowler, E 1963
Stevenson, R B K and Emery, J 1964, 206-11
Stevenson, R B K 1976
Clarke, D V and Ralston, I B M 1978, no 49

Found whilst digging in the ring cairn within a recumbent stone circle shortly before 1840.

Length (A) 142mm: diameter (B) c 66mm: Length (C) 273mm
On loan from the National Museum of Antiquities of Scotland
Catalogue numbers: L1962.128-130

26
Double link silver chain
Parkhill, Newmachar, Aberdeenshire

This is one of two massive silver chains which display decoration in a Pictish style. The other eight comparable examples are essentially plain (see no 32). Engraved designs, once filled with red enamel, traces of which remain, are confined to the end-ring of the Parkhill chain and consist of the 's' and triple-disc symbols, paralleled on some of the carved stones. The 's' symbol is nonetheless comparatively rare, occurring on only four stones, two from Sutherland and two from Aberdeenshire, as well as on the wall of Doo cave in Fife (Shepherd and Shepherd, 1978, 218: Henderson, 1979).

Such chains are likely to have been worn as necklets. The links of the chain will only pass through the end-ring one at a time, thereby offering a secure method of fixing the jewellery around the wearer's neck. In all, the chain weighs approximately 1.25 kg.

To make it, the silversmith would have begun by forming the metal into rods. These would then have been hammered to the required shape over a template. The links would then have been inserted, and the ends hammered together to complete the manufacture.

This chain was probably made in about the 7th century. The other decorated chain, from Whitecleugh, Lanarkshire, is likely to be of similar date, given the form of the symbols with which it is decorated, and taking into account a similar design on the silver plaques from the Norrie's Law hoard in Fife.

Stuart, J 1856
Smith, J A 1874, 330-2
Smith, J A 1881a, 66-7
Anderson, J 1881, 43
Mitchell, A 1902, 32
Anderson, J and Allen J R 1903c, 199
Thomas, A C 1963, 44-5
Clarke, D V and Ralston, I B M, 1978, no 51
Henderson, I M 1979.

The chain was found whilst trenching 1 mile east of the now-disused Parkhill railway station in 1894.

Length 502mm
Diameter of rings 32mm approximately
On loan from the National Museum of Antiquities of Scotland
Catalogue number: FC 147

27
Steatite beads
Aberdeenshire

(a) Bourtie
(b) No precise location
(c) Knockenbaird, Insch
(d) No precise location

These steatite or 'soapstone' beads represent imitations of the annular glass beads which were in use in the early centuries AD. The stone copies may have begun to be made by the first century, and production may have continued into the Dark Ages. The grey-streaked creamy steatite is likely to have been obtained from the Portsoy area of Banffshire. A bead in this material was found at the Cullykhan promontory fort, and a further example comes from the Severan-period Roman base at Carpow on the Tay. The hoard of charms from Cairnhill, Monquhitter, included an egg-shaped object in this material, which was also used to produce a number of items recovered from the upper layers at Traprain Law (Stevenson, 1967), a site probably abandoned after 450.

Other stone copies of beads, some made of lithomarge, have been recovered from Scottish mainland sites, including some with Roman occupation. The examples displayed here have no useful associations.

Glaister, J 1911, vol 2, 863, no 3
Stevenson, R B K and Collins, G H 1976
Guido, M 1978, 89

All four beads were in Dr J G Callander's collection by 1911, and were bequeathed by him to the Museum, Marischal College in 1938.

Diameters: (a) 26mm (b) 24mm (c) 22mm (d) 23mm

Catalogue numbers: all ABDUA (a) 15510
(b) 15511
(c) 15522
(d) 15527

28
Bronze loose-ring pins
Culbean Hill, near Dinnet, Aberdeenshire

Undecorated ring-headed pins made of bronze were in use in North Britain for several centuries. The earliest examples are those in which the plane of the head stands proud of the shaft—so-called 'projecting ring-headed pins'. These date to the pre-Roman Iron Age. Thereafter, variants continued to develop, particularly, although not exclusively, in Ireland.

These two plain-ringed, loop-headed pins, found together near the group of hut-circles on Culbean Hill (Ogston, 1931), overlooking the Howe of Cromar, are likely to be of more recent date. Indications of this are furnished by the flattened shank, and broad loop to attach the ring, visible on one of the pins. These features suggest a date around the 9th century for manufacture.

The tradition of fastening clothes using pins, as opposed to buttons or toggles, is usually diagnostic of the wearing of loosely-woven garments. When in use, such pins would have been secured to the garment by a thong running from the ring to the tip of the pin. Fanning (1983) considers that some of them served as 'shroud fasteners'.

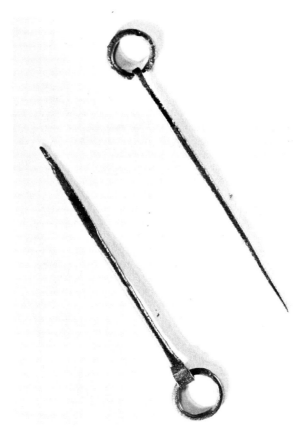

Gifted to the Museum, Marischal College, by Dr A MacAldowie in 1894. They are not mentioned in Ogston's subsequent discussion of the Culblean sites.

Length: (a) 145mm (b) 149 mm
Ring diameter: (a) 25mm, (b) 22.5mm
Catalogue numbers: both ABDUA (a) 15549
(b) 15550

29
Glass beads
Aberdeenshire and Moray

(a) Culbin Sands, Moray
(b) Kildrummy, Aberdeenshire
(c) Tap o' Noth, Rhynie, Aberdeenshire
(d-f) Aberdeenshire

These beads, in common with annular beads in a similar range of colours, are believed to have been the products of local craftsmen, although southern inspiration may have partly conditioned their style. They were made by twisting different colours of glass together, and then marvering the results into shape whilst the glass was still molten. This latter process, often rather roughly accomplished, contributed to their rather irregular shape.

Such North Scottish spiral-decorated beads (Guido, 1978, Class 13) have been recovered from souterrains and brochs, and two examples are known from Burghead. Beads of this kind have on occasion been found with annular examples. Referred to as 'Pictish beads' by Laing (1974, 197-8), their distribution is concentrated between the Laigh of Moray and the Dee. They may have been produced essentially in the first century AD in Guido's view, but Laing notes their occurrence in the hoard from Croy, Inverness-shire, deposited c 850.

Wilson, D 1851, 303
Michie, J 1887, 11-12 (b)
Glaister, J 1911, vol 2, 863, no 3 (a)
Reid, R W 1912, I-382
Laing, L 1974, 197-8
Laing, L 1975
Guido, M 1978, 85-7 and 193-7

Most similar pins from Scotland have been recovered from Viking graves, particularly in the Western Isles. One, with a flattened shank, comes from the Lower Norse horizon at the Brough of Birsay (Curle, 1982, 62, no 422). Examples from mainland Scotland include finds at Reay in Caithness, Sandwood bay in Sutherland, and from Kirkcudbright, as well as an example from the vitrified fort of the Doune of Relugas in Moray.

Glaister, J 1911, vol 2, 866 no 17
Reid, R W 1912, no I 389
Stevenson, R B K 1955b, 292
Laing, L R 1975
Fanning, T 1983

(a) were bequeathed to the Anthropological Museum by Dr J G Callander in 1938, (b) was gifted by Rev Prof J Christie in 1866, (c) by Mrs D H Fraser in 1970, and (f) by Christ's Church College in 1952.

Dimensions: (a) 15.5mm (b) 14.5mm (c) 17.5mm (d) 22mm (e) 18mm (f) 13.5mm

Catalogue numbers: all ABDUA   (a) 15507
      (b) 17435
      (c) 15590
      (d) 15542
      (e) 15543
      (f) 15541

(c)-(f) are unpublished

30
Sculptured stone fragment
Kineddar Old Manse, Drainie, Moray

The Laigh of Moray, between Forres and Elgin, is unique in the North-East in having figure carving dating from the 9th and 10th centuries in any quantity. The major extant sculpture dating to this period is Sueno's Stone, which is unparalleled in scale in the area. However, this sandstone fragment, found with others during the demolition of the Old Manse of Kineddar, may have formed part of a similar monument. With the exception of one piece of a Class I stone, none of the other fragments from Kineddar displays Pictish symbols, suggesting that the remainder of the sculpture belongs to Class III. A suitable patron for such accomplished work might have been an early ecclesiastic, since Drainie seems to have been an important centre prior to the establishment of the bishopric at Spynie and subsequently in Elgin.

The serried ranks of warriors, carved in relief, are a witness of the sculptor's knowledge of Irish prototypes, such as Muiredach's Cross at Monasterboice in Co Louth. This sculpture thus provides a further indication of increasing Scotic/Irish influence well inside Pictland during the 9th and 10th centuries.

Stuart, J 1856, pl CXXIX, no 13
Anderson, J and Allen, J R 1903c, 148 (=Drainie 13)
Stevenson, R B K 1955a
Henderson, I M 1978

One of the numerous fragments recovered during the demolition of the house and walled garden of the Old Manse at Kineddar in 1855. Presented to Elgin Museum in the same year.

Height 440mm: width 520mm

On loan from the Moray Society

Catalogue number: Elgin 1855.1.6

31

Sculptured stone fragment
Kineddar Manse, Drainie, Moray

This sandstone, like no 30, once formed part of a larger cross slab. The depiction of the foot soldier is heavily stylised and shows him carrying both a large spear and a small round shield. The shaft of the former is distinctly more solid than depicted on the recently-discovered slab from Barflat, near Rhynie (Shepherd and Shepherd, 1978). The original of the shield was probably wooden. Both weapons may be considered favourite elements of Dark Age weaponry.

This sculplture is likely to date on stylistic grounds to the end of the Pictish period, when Scotic influences were becoming more marked. This process culminated

politically in the accession of Kenneth mac Alpin to the kingdom of the Picts in the mid-9th century, but need not have been consolidated in terms of cultural influences for some time thereafter.

Stuart, J 1856, pl CXXX no 1
Anderson, J and Allen, J R 1903c, 145
Stevenson, R B K 1955a
Stevenson, R B K 1971
Henderson, I M 1978

This fragment was found, with thirty others, during the demolition of the Old Manse and adjoining garden walls in 1855. It was presented to Elgin Museum in the same year.

Height 260mm: width 160mm
On loan from the Moray Society
Catalogue number: Elgin 1855.1.13

32

Double link silver chain fragment
North promontory, Nigg Bay, St Fitticks,
Kincardineshire

When discovered in the late 18th century, this chain was some 60cm long and had a penannular ring at one end: the finder thought that the chain had been buried hastily, possibly in a cloth bag which had subsequently decayed. Analysis of the surviving part revealed that the silver content of the object was 95%, a much higher figure than for modern sterling silver. It has been suggested that some of the chains may be made of melted-down Roman silver-gilt objects (Henderson, 1967, 212).

Such chains, directly associated with kingship in Wales (Ross, 1959; Enright, 1983), are clearly an indication of wealth or status. Attribution to the Picts is based partly on geographical distribution, but more particularly on the occurrence of Pictish symbols on two examples (see no 26). A date in the seventh century may be suggested for manufacture, but an earlier date cannot be ruled out.

British, rather than a Pictish, product (Enright, 1983), but the symbols on the Whitecleugh and Parkhill examples would need to be later addenda in this case.

Smith, J A 1874
Glaister, J 1911, vol 2, 865, no 5
Reid, R W 1912
Edwards, A J H 1939
Henderson, I M 1979

This object was found by a Mr Edward whilst digging on the headland overlooking Nigg Bay. He gave it to Mr Jonathan Troup, who in turn presented it to the Museum, Marischal College, on August 14th, 1796.

Length 115mm: Diameter of rings 33mm

Catalogue number: ABDUA 15644

33
Whetstone
Portsoy, Banffshire

Whilst whetstones are common objects in metal-using cultures, decorated examples such as this are extremely rare. The Portsoy example is the only one decorated with human heads to have been found in the Pictish area, but it is paralleled further south by a single example from Dumfriesshire, and five from England. Stylistic considerations may support a date late in the 6th century or in the 7th century for objects of this type. In contrast with most depictions of the human face in Pictish art, these examples are shown frontally, and not in profile. One head has an uneven Latin cross below it, and other symbols include a fish and a plain crescent. The reverse displays a further fish.

Geologically, the stone is of a type foreign to North-East Scotland, and this may be taken to support a place of manufacture in the Scottish borderland, or indeed further South. It may thus be considered as a Celtic product, produced by a craftsman in the area of one of the old British kingdoms, such as Gododdin in South-East Scotland, or Strathclyde, further West (Enright, 1983). In this case, the subsidiary decoration may have

The majority of such chains have been found in Scotland south of the Tay (Edwards, 1939: Henderson, 1979, fig 1), but no single mechanism to explain how they got there has been accepted. For Henderson, this distribution may reflect political circumstances in the later 7th century, when southern Pictland was under Anglian domination. It is sometimes suggested that they may have been a been incised subsequently. However, the discovery of a formerly-gilded bronze pin at Golspie, Sutherland, which carries a face (also with a furrowed brow) seen full on, provides a comparable image. It is thus possible that the Portsoy whetstone is an entirely Pictish product.

A tentative interpretation of the symbolism may be attempted. The human head was of major significance in the mythology—and, by extension, in the art—of Celtic peoples. It was envisaged as the seat of regenerative seed, and was moreover believed to be capable of life, independent of the body. The whetstone itself is phallic in form, emphasising this connection with life. Conversely, death may be indicated by the inversion of the lower head, such that the two heads may have been combined to indicate the bearer's power over life and death. The presence of metalsmith's tongs on this item may also be significant, since the importance of the smith relative to the 'king' was often considerable, and was cloaked in semi-mystical associations. A broadly similar object from the Anglo-Saxon royal burial at Sutton Hoo has been interpreted as a sceptre—a token of power—and its mythical associations examined (Simpson, 1979).

It is conceivable that the Portsoy whetstone fulfilled a similar function. Whatever the interpretation of the symbolism, the likelihood is that this object was an indication of status, and not simply a decorated version of an everyday object. Although the essence of the decoration of this object appears Celtic in inspiration, nothing prevents it from having retained its significance in Pictland.

Thomas, A C 1963, 48 pl II
Ross, A 1967
Close-Brooks, J 1975, pl 27
Simpson, J 1979
Enright, M 1983

Nothing is known of the circumstances of the discovery of this object.

Length: 143m

On loan from the British Museum
Catalogue number: 1921, 7-9, 1

34
Shale pin heads and bronze objects
Hill of Crichie, Inverurie, Aberdeenshire

These objects were found under a large stone, near the hill-fort of Bruce's Camp. It is uncertain whether they accompanied a burial, as there is no record of a body, although the find was described as 'cist-like'. They may have been interred for ritual or other reasons.

As well as 13 (not 7 *pace* MacGregor, 1976, 177) of these bobble heads for pins, a bronze ferrule (knob) for the butt of a spear-shaft and a bronze terret of Donside type were also found. That the shale items served as pins is supported by the fact that some examples retain a portion of an iron shaft. A broadly similar, although smaller, bobble head, in this case associated with a bronze shank, comes from Dinas Powys in North Wales, and led Alcock to argue for a fifth century date for the Crichie find (Alcock, 1963, 177 and fn 4). However, similar items are recorded from 'pre-Severan' contexts at Traprain, and the type is paralleled in bone on certain broch sites (Stevenson, 1955b, 292-3), and, at a rather later date, in Buston crannog. Since Stevenson wrote, further examples of bobble-headed pins of later date have come to light. Somewhat similar bone pins, again with iron shanks, are considered residual finds in Viking contexts at the Brough of Birsay (Curle, 1982, 50, and ill 38, nos 259-62), and the type also occurs in fifth/sixth century contexts at the Mote of Mark in SW Scotland (Laing, pers comm).

The terret, of Donside type, has an iron bar recessed in the base The spear-butt, (MacGregor, 1976, no 177) is of 'door-knob' type, in which the shaft or ferrule is differentiated from the terminal knob by a rib. The mouth of the ferrule is edged by two engraved lines. A more elaborate version of this latter type of object was found, accompanied by stone cups and other items, in a broch at Harray on Orkney (Anderson, 1883, 236, and fig 208), and moulds for their production came from the forts of Dunagoil on Bute and Traprain Law in East Lothian. For Childe (1935,

228), this is the type of spear-butt to which reference is made in Dio Cassius' description of the early third century Severan campaigns in Scotland. A date in the 3rd or 4th century may be suggested for this material.

We may only speculate as to whether the deposition of this material bears any relation to the much earlier, and now much-decayed, ritual complex at Broomend of Crichie: it may be noted, however, that one of the stones from an 'avenue' at Crichie bears Pictish symbols.

Chalmers, J H 1867, 110-4
Callander, J G 1906, 35
Smith, R A 1925, 158-9
Kilbride-Jones, H E 1935
MacGregor, M 1976, no 116 and no 177

Found while 'trenching' on the Hill of Crichie in 1856. The major part of the collection was gifted to the Museum, Marischal College, by Capt I P H Chalmers in 1927.

Ferrule: 39mm × 54mm. Terret 74mm × 63.5mm

Four bobble heads, terret, and ferrule on loan from the British Museum

Catalogue numbers: none

Diameter: Aberdeen pin-heads (average) 34mm

Catalogue number: ABDUA 15645

35
Annular glass bead
Castle Hill, Kintore, Aberdeenshire

Plain annular beads of this type were in use in southern Britain from about the 1st century BC until the 6th century AD. Very few examples have been recovered in Scotland, although two sites, Traprain Law in East Lothian and the Sculptor's Cave at Covesea in Moray, have produced comparable beads. At the latter site, the beads were recovered from the 'Roman period' occupation horizon (Benton, 1931); they were thought likely to have been made of re-used Roman glass. Blue-green glass was often used for 'bottles' and similar containers in the Roman world. It is possible that chemical analyses may help in refining the chronologies for such beads (Warner and Meighan, 1981).

Sadly, it is difficult to make much of the context from which the Kintore bead was recovered. The 'Castle Hill' was destroyed during the construction of the railway in mid-Victorian times. It is conceivable that the 'Hill' was originally a prehistoric cairn. More pertinently, two sculptured stones, now in the National Museum of Antiquities in Edinburgh, were removed from a burnt layer which contained some bone material. These are decorated with a number of symbols in Class I style. It is thus possible that the mound continued to be used for ritual or burial during the Pictish period.

Glaister, J 1911, vol 2, 863, no 3
Guido, M 1978, 66

Bequeathed to the Museum, Marischal College, by Dr J G Callander in 1938, in whose collection it was by 1911.

Diameter: 18mm

Catalogue number: ABDUA 15519

Unpublished

References

Abercromby, J, 1904, 'Explorations of Circular Enclosures and an Underground House near Dinnet on Deeside' *Proc Soc Antiq Scot,* 38, 1903-4, 102-22

Alcock, L, 1963, *Dinas Powys: an Iron Age, Dark Age and Early Medieval Settlement in Glamorgan*

Alcock, L, 1980, 'Populi bestiales Pictorum feroci animo: a survey of Pictish settlement archaeology' in *eds* Hanson, W S and Keppie, L J F *Roman Frontier Studies,* 1979, vol 1, 61-95 Brit Archaeol Rep, 71, i

Alcock, L, 1981a, 'Early historic fortifications in Scotland' in *ed* Guilbert, G *Hill-Fort Studies,* 150-80

Alcock, L, 1981b, 'Early historic Fortifications of Scotland' *Current Archaeol,* no 79, 230-6

Alcock, L, 1982, 'Forteviot: a Pictish and Scottish Royal Church and Palace' in *ed* Pearce, S M, *The Early Church in Western Britain and Ireland,* 211-39. Brit Archaeol Rep, 102

Alcock, L, 1983 *Cadbury-Camelot: a fifteen-year perspective* (=*Proc Brit Acad,* 68, 1982, 357-88)

Anderson, A O, 1922, *Early Sources of Scottish History AD 500-1286,* 2 vols

Anderson, A O & Anderson, M O, 1961, *Adamnan's Life of Columba*

Anderson, M O, 1973 *Kings and Kingship in Early Scotland* 2 edn, 1980

Anderson, J, 1881, *Scotland in Early Christian Times* 2nd series

Anderson, J, 1883, *Scotland in Pagan Times: the Iron Age*

Anderson, J, 1902, 'Notice of Cists discovered in a Cairn at Cairnhill, Parish of Monquhitter, Aberdeenshire and at Doune, Perthshire' *Proc Soc Antiq Scot,* 36, 1901-2, 675-88

Anderson, J & Allen, J Romilly, 1903, *The Early Christian Monuments of Scotland,* Society of Antiquaries of Scotland, 3 vols

Angus-Butterworth, L M, 1967, 'Ancient Pictish Monuments in Angus and Perthshire' *Trans Anc Monuments Soc,* 14, 39-56

Ashmore, P J, 1980, 'Low cairns, long cists and symbol stones' *Proc Soc Antiq Scot,* 110, 1978-80, 346-55.

Benton, S, 1931, 'The Excavation of the Sculptor's Cave, Covesea, Morayshire' *Proc Soc Antiq Scot,* 65, 1930-1, 177-216

Breeze, D J, 1982, *The Northern Frontiers of Roman Britain*

Bulloch, J, 1971, 'The Church in Celtic Scotland and the Native Culture' in Meldrum, 25-36

Burley, E, 1956, 'A Survey and Catalogue of the Metalwork from Traprain Law' *Proc Soc Antiq Scot,* 89, 1955-6, 118-226

Callander, J G, 1906, 'A Late Celtic Harness Mounting of Bronze from Culsalmond' *Proc Soc Antiq Scot,* 40, 1905-6, 33-5

Callander, J G, 1915, 'Notice of a Bronze Cup and other Objects found apparently in a Sepulchral Deposit near Tarland, Aberdeenshire' *Proc Soc Antiq Scot,* 49, 1914-5, 203-6

Callander, J G, 1916, 'Notices of (1) Three Stone Cups found in a Cairn in Aberdeenshire, and (2) a Short Cist . . . at Boglehill Wood, Longniddry, East Lothian' *Proc Soc Antiq Scot,* 50, 1915-6, 145-51

Callander J G, 1927, 'An Early Iron Age Hoard from Crichie, near Inverurie' *Proc Soc Antiq Scot,* 61, 1926-7, 234-6

Chalmers, J H, 1867, 'Notice on the Discovery of a Stone Cist at Broomend, near Inverurie, Aberdeenshire' *Proc Soc Antiq Scot,* 7, 1866-7, 110-4

eds Chapman, J C & Mytum, H C, 1983, *Settlement in North Britain, 1000BC-AD1000,* Brit Archaeol Rep Brit Ser, 118

Childe, V G, 1935, *The Prehistory of Scotland*

Clarke, D V & Ralston, I B M, 1978, *Ancient Treasures of Scotland,* Art Galleries & Museum, Aberdeen

Close-Brooks, J, 1975, 'A Pictish Pin from Golspie, Sutherland' *Proc Soc Antiq Scot,* 106, 1974-5, 208-10

Coles, F R 1905, 'Report on Stone Circles in Aberdeenshire' *Proc Soc Antiq Scot,* 39, 1904-5, 206-18

Cowan, I B 1975, 'Early Ecclesiastical Foundations' in *ed* McNeill, P and Nicholson, R *An Historical Atlas of Scotland,* 17-9

Cowie, T 1978, 'Excavations at the Catstane, Midlothian, 1977' *Proc Soc Antiq Scot*, 109, 1977-8, 166-201

Cramp, R 1978, 'The Anglian tradition' in Lang, 1-32

Crawford, I A & Switsur, R, 1977, 'Sandscaping and C14: the Udal, N Uist' *Antiq*, 51, 124-36

Cruden, S H, 1964, *The Early Christian Monuments of Scotland*, 2 edn

Cunliffe, B W, 1978, *Iron Age Communities in Britain*, rev edn

Curle, C L, 1940, 'The Chronology of the Early Christian Monuments of Scotland' *Proc Soc Antiq Scot*, 74, 1939-40, 60-115

Curle, C L, 1982, *Pictish and Norse Finds from the Brough of Birsay, 1934-74 = Soc Antiq Scot Monog Ser*, 1

Curle, J, 1932, 'An Inventory of Objects of Roman and Provincial Origin found on Sites in Scotland not definitely associated with Roman Constructions' *Proc Soc Antiq Scot*, 66, 1931-2, 277-397

Diack, F C, 1944, *The Inscriptions of Pictland*, Third Spalding Club, Aberdeen

Donaldson, G, 1972, *Church and Nation through Sixteen Centuries*

Duncan, A A M, 1975, *Scotland: the Making of the Kingdom*, The Edinburgh History of Scotland, 1

Easson, D E & Cowan, I B, 1976, *Medieval Religious Houses in Scotland*

Edwards, A J H, 1939, 'A massive double-linked Silver Chain' *Proc Soc Antiq Scot*, 73, 1938-9, 326-7

Edwards, K J & Ralston, I B M, 1978, 'New dating and environmental evidence from Burghead fort, Moray' *Proc Soc Antiq Scot*, 109, 1977-8, 202-10

Edwards, K J, 1979, 'Palynological and temporal inference in the context of prehistory, with special reference to the evidence from lake and peat deposits' *Journ Archaeol Sci*, 6, 255-70

Enright, M J, 1983, 'The Sutton Hoo whetstone sceptre: a study of inconography and cultural milieu' *Anglo-Saxon England*, 11, 119-34

Fanning, T, 1983, 'Some aspects of the bronze ringed pin in Scotland' in O'Connor & Clarke, 324-42

Feachem, R W, 1955, 'Fortifications' in Wainwright, 66-86

Feachem, R W, 1966, 'The hill-forts of northern Britain' in Rivet, 59-87

Fojut, N and Love, P, forthcoming, 'Excavations at Dundarg Castle, 1981' *Proc Soc Antiq Scot*

Fowler, E, 1963, 'Celtic metalwork of the fifth and sixth centuries' *Archaeol J*, 120, 98-160

Fox, C F, 1958, *Pattern and Purpose: a survey of Celtic Art in Britain*

Galbraith, J D, *St Machar's Cathedral: the Celtic Antecedents* Friends of St Machar's Cathedral Occas Pap, 8

Glaister, J, 1911, *The Palace of History; Scottish Exhibition*, Glasgow, 2 vols

Gordon, C A, 1966, 'The Pictish Animals Observed' *Proc Soc Antiq Scot*, 98, 1964-6, 215-24

Graham-Campbell, J, 1973, 'The 9th Century Anglo-Saxon Horn Mount from Burghead, Morayshire, Scotland' *Medieval Archaeol*, 17, 43-51

Guido, M, 1978, *The Glass Beads of the Prehistoric and Roman Periods in Britain and Ireland = Res Rep Soc Antiq Lond*, 35

Gurnell, J, 1884, *The Standing Stones of the District* (= Huntly)

Greig, J C, 1970, 'Excavations at Castle Point, Troup' *Aberdeen Univ Rev*, no 143, 274-83

Greig, J C, 1972, 'Cullykhan' *Current Archaeol*, no 32, 1972, 227-31

Hawkes, C F C, 1951, 'Bronze-workers, Cauldrons and Bucket-animals in Iron Age and Roman Britain' in ed Grimes, W F *Aspects of Archaeology in Britain and Abroad*, 172-99

Hedges, J & Bell, B, 1980, 'The Howe' *Current Archaeol*, no 73, 48-51

Henderson, I M, 1958, 'The Origin Centre of the Pictish Symbol Stones' *Proc Soc Antiq Scot*, 91, 1957-8, 53-67

Henderson, I M, 1967, *The Picts*

Henderson, I M, 1971, 'The Meaning of the Pictish Symbol Stones' in Meldrum, 53-67

Henderson, I M, 1972, 'The Picts of Aberdeenshire and their Monuments' *Archaeol J*, 129, 166-74

Henderson, I M, 1975, 'Inverness, a Pictish Capital' in ed Meldrum, E *The Hub of the Highlands,* 91-108. Inverness Field Club Centenary Volume

Henderson, I M, 1978, 'Sculpture North of the Forth after the Take-over by the Scots' in Lang, 47-73

Henderson, I M, 1979, 'The Silver Chain from Whitecleugh, Shieldholm, Crawfordjohn, Lanarkshire' *Trans Dumfries Galloway Nat Hist Antiq Soc,* 54, 20-8

Henderson, I M, 1980, 'Pictish art in the Book of Kells' in eds Whitelock, D, Dumville, D and McKitterick, R *Ireland and Early Medieval Europe,* 79-105

Henderson, I M, 1983, 'Pictish vine-scroll ornament' in O'Connor and Clarke, 243-268

Hogg, A H A, 1975, *Hill-Forts of Britain*

Hope-Taylor, B K, 1977, *Yeavering: an Anglo-British Centre of early Northumbria* Dept Environment Archaeol Rep, 7

Hope-Taylor, B K, 1980 'Balbridie . . . and Doon Hill' *Current Archaeol,* no 72, 18-9

Hunter, J R, 1984, 'Pool Bay—the story so far' *Archaeology Extra,* no 1 (University of Bradford)

Inglis, J C, & Inglis, R B, forthcoming 'A symbol stone from the Dead Man's Howe, Wantonwells, Insch, Grampian'

Jackson, K H, 1955, 'The Pictish language' in Wainwright, 129-60

Jackson, K H, 1972, *The Gaelic Notes in the Book of Deer*

Keppie, L J F, 1981, 'Mons Graupius: the search for a battlefield' *Scot Archaeol Forum,* 12, 79-88

Kilbride-Jones, H E, 1935, 'An Aberdeenshire Iron Age Miscellany' *Proc Soc Antiq Scot,* 69, 1934-5, 445-54

Kilbride-Jones, H E, 1980, *Celtic Craftsmanship in Bronze*

Laing, L R, 1974, 'Picts, Saxons and Celtic metalwork' *Proc Soc Antiq Scot,* 105, 1972-4, 189-99

Laing, L R, 1975, *The Archaeology of Late Celtic Britain and Ireland*

Laing, L R, & Laing, J, forthcoming, 'The date and origin of the Pictish symbols' *Proc Soc Antiq Scot*

ed Lang, J, 1978, *Anglo-Saxon and Viking Age Sculpture* Brit Archaeol Rep, 49

Lauder, T D, 1831, 'Description of . . . Relic . . . Found near . . . Findhorn' *Archaeologia Scotica,* 3, 1831, 99-102

Leeds, E T, 1933, *Celtic Ornament in the British Isles*

Longley, D, 1975, *Hanging-Bowls, Penannular Brooches, and the Anglo-Saxon Connexion* Brit Archaeol Rep, 22

Macbain, A, 1886, 'The Book of Deer' *Trans Gaelic Soc Inverness,* 11, 1885-6

Macdonald, A D S and Laing, L R, 1970, 'Early Ecclesiastical Sites in Scotland: a Field survey, Part II' *Proc Soc Antiq Scot,* 102, 1969-70, 129-45

Macdonald, J, 1862, 'Historical Notices of the "The Broch" of Burghead, in Moray, with an Account of its Antiquities' *Proc Soc Antiq Scot,* 4, 1860-2, 321-69

MacGregor, M, 1976, *Early Celtic Art in North Britain,* 2 vols

MacLagan, C, 1875, *The Hill-Forts, Stone Circles and Other Remains of Ancient Scotland*

Maxwell, G S, 1981, 'Agricola's campaigns: the evidence of the temporary camps' *Scot Archaeol Forum,* 12, 25-54

Maxwell, G S, 1983, 'Recent aerial survey in Scotland' in ed Maxwell, G S, *The Impact of Aerial Reconnaissance on Archaeology, Counc Brit Archaeol Res Rep,* 49, 27-40

Megaw, J V S, 1970, *Art of the European Iron Age*

Michie, J, 1887, *Catalogue of Antiquities in the Archaeological Museum,* King's College, Aberdeen

Miller, M, 1980, 'Hiberni reversuri', *Proc Soc Antiq Scot,* 110, 1978-80, 305-27

Mitchell, A, 1884, 'Vacation notes in Burghead, Cromar and Strathspey' *Proc Soc Antiq Scot,* 10, 1872-4, 603-89

Mitchell, A, 1902, 'Prehistory of the Scottish Area: Fifty Years' Work of the Society of Antiquities of Scotland' *Proc Soc Antiq Scot,* 36, 1901-2, 11-65

Morris, J, 1973, *The Age of Arthur* 2 edn, 1975

eds O'Connor, A, & Clarke, D V, 1983 *From the Stone Age to the 'Forty-Five'*

O'Dell, A C, 1960, *St Ninian's Isle Treasure* Aberdeen Univ Studies, 141

Ogston, A, 1931, *The Prehistoric Antiquities of the Howe of Cromar* Third Spalding Club, Aberdeen

Piggott, S, 1955, *'The Archaelogical Background'* in Wainwright, 54-65

Piggott, S, 1970, *Early Celtic Art*

Raftery, B, 1980 'Iron Age Cauldrons in Ireland' *Archaelogia Atlantica*, 3, 58-67

Ralston, I B M, 1980, 'The Green Castle and the promontory-forts of North-East Scotland' *Scot Archaeol Forum*, 10, 27-40

Ralston, I B M, 1982, 'A timber hall at Balbridie Farm' *Aberdeen Univ Rev*, no 168, 238-49

Ralston, I B M, 1983, 'Relationships between archaeological sites and geomorphology in the coastal zone of the North-East Scotland' in *ed* Ritchie, W, *North East Scotland Coastal Field Guide and Geographical Essays*, 111-25

Ralston, I B M, 1984, 'Notes on the archaeology of Kincardine and Deeside' *The Deeside Field, forthcoming*

Raslton, I B M, Sabine, K A & Watt, W G, 1983, 'Later prehistoric settlements in North-East Scotland: a preliminary assessment' in Chapman and Mytum, 149-73

Reid, R W, 1912, Illustrated Catalogue, Anthropological Museum, University of Aberdeen

Reynolds, N M, 1980, 'Dark Age Timber Halls and the Background to Excavation at Balbridie' *Scot Archaeol Forum*, 10, 41-60

ed Richmond, I A, 1958, *Roman and Native in North Britain*

Ritchie, A, 1977, 'Excavation of Pictish and Viking-Age Farmsteads at Buckquoy, Orkney' *Proc Soc Antiq Scot*, 108, 1976-7, 174-227

Ritchie, G & Ritchie, A, 1981, *Scotland: Archaeology and Early History* Ancient Peoples and Places, 99

Ritchie, J, 1915, 'Notes on some Aberdeenshire Stones and Crosses' *Proc Soc Antiq Scot*, 49, 1914-5, 33-49

ed Rivet, A L F, 1966, *The Iron Age in North Britain*

Rivet, A L F & Smith, C, 1979, *The Place-names of Roman Britain*

Robertson, A, 1970, 'Roman finds from non-Roman Sites in Scotland' *Britannia*, 1, 198-226

Ross, A, 1959, 'Chain Symbolism in Pagan Celtic Religion' *Speculum*, 34, 39-59

Ross, A, 1967, *Pagan Celtic Britain*

Shepherd, I A G, 1981, 'Bronze Age Jet Working in North Britain' *Scot Archaeol Forum*, 11, 43-51

Shepherd, I A G, 1983, 'Pictish settlement problems in NE Scotland' in Chapman and Mytum, 327-56

Shepherd, I A G & Shepherd, A N, 1978, 'An incised Pictish figure and a new symbol stone from Barflat, Rhynie, Gordon District' *Proc Soc Antiq Scot*, 109, 1977-8, 211-22

Simpson, J, 1979, 'The King's Whetstone' *Antiq*, 53, 96-101

Simpson, M, 1968, 'Massive Armlets in the North British Iron Age' in Coles, J M and Simpson, D D A, *Studies in Ancient Europe*, 233-54

Simpson, W D, 1925, *The Origins of Christianity in Aberdeenshire*

Simpson, W D, 1943, *The Province of Mar, Aberdeen Univ Studies*, 121

Simpson, W D, 1954, *Dundarg Castle, Aberdeen Univ Studies*, 131

Simpson, W D, 1960, 'Dundarg Castle reconsidered' *Trans Buchan Field Club*, 17, part iv, 9-25

Simpson, W D, 1971, *Dunnottar Castle: historical and descriptive*, 12 edn

Small, A, 1962, '[A Pictish Stone from] Fairgreen, Collace, Perthshire, with a note on a stone cup from the same farm' *Proc Soc Antiq Scot*, 95, 1961-2, 221-2

Small, A, 1969, 'Burghead' *Scot Archaeol Forum*, 1, 61-8

Small, A, Thomas, C and Wilson, D, 1973, *St Ninian's Isle and its Treasure*, 2 vols, *Aberdeen Univ Studies*, 152

Smith, J A, 1874, 'Notice of a Silver Chain . . . in the Possession of the University of Aberdeen, and of other Ancient Scottish Silver Chains' *Proc Soc Antiq Scot*, 10, 1872-4, 321-47

Smith, J A, 1881a, '. . . Notes of Similar Chains found in Scotland' *Proc Soc Antiq Scot,* 15, 1880-1, 64-70

Smith, J A, 1881b, 'Notice of a Massive Bronze "Late Celtic" Armlet . . .' *Proc Soc Antiq Scot,* 15, 1880-1, 316-61

Smith, R A, 1925, *A Guide to the Antiquities of the Early Iron Age* British Museum, London, 2 edn

Stead, I, 1967, 'A La Tene III Burial at Welwyn Garden City' *Archaeologia,* 101, 1-62

Steer, K A, 1956, 'An Early Iron Age Homestead at West Plean, Stirlingshire' *Proc Soc Antiq Scot,* 89, 1955-6, 227-49

Stevenson, R B K, 1949, 'The Nuclear Fort of Dalmahoy, and other Dark Age Capitals' *Proc Soc Antiq Scot,* 83, 1948-9, 186-97

Stevenson, R B K, 1955a, 'Pictish Art' in Wainwright, 97-128

Stevenson, R B K, 1955b, 'Pins and the Chronology of the Brochs' *Proc Prehist Soc,* 21, 282-94

Stevenson, R B K, 1959, 'The Inchyra Stone and Some Other Unpublished Early Christian Monuments' *Proc Soc Antiq Scot,* 92, 1958-9, 33-55

Stevenson, R B K, 1966, 'Metalwork and some other objects in Scotland and their cultural affinities' in Rivet, 17-44

Stevenson, R B K, 1967, 'A Roman-period Cache of Charms in Aberdeenshire' *Antiq,* 41, 143-5

Stevenson, R B K, 1971, 'Sculptures in Scotland in the 6th-9th Centuries AD' *Kolloquium uber spatantike und fruhmittelalterische Skulptur,* 2, 65-74 (Mainz)

Stevenson, R B K, 1976, 'The Earlier metalwork of Pictland' in *ed* Megaw, J V S, *To illustrate the Monuments,* 246-51

Stevenson, R B K, & Emery, J, 1964, 'The Gaulcross Hoard of Pictish Silver' *Proc Soc Antiq Scot,* 97, 1963-4, 206-11

Stevenson, R B K, & Collins, G H, 1976, 'Beads of reddish marbled stone (lithomarge)' *Glasgow Archaeol J,* 4, 55-6

Stuart, J, 1856, *The Sculptured Stones of Scotland,* vol 1

Stuart, J, 1867, *The Sculptured Stones of Scotland,* vol 2

Taylor, D B, 1982, 'Excavation of a promontory fort, broch and souterrain at Hurly Hawkin, Angus' *Proc Soc Antiq Scot,* 112, 215-53

Thomas, A C, 1961, 'The Animal Art of the Scottish Iron Age and its Origins' *Archaeol J,* 118, 14-64

Thomas, A C, 1963, 'The interpretation of the Pictish symbols' *Archaeol J,* 120, 30-97

Thomas, A C, 1967, 'The Evidence from North Britain' in *eds* Barley, M W and Hanson, R P C, *Christianity in Britain, 300-700,* 93-121

Thomas, A C, 1971, *The Early Christian Archaeology of North Britain*

Thomas, A C, 1981, *A provisional list of imported pottery in post-Roman Western Britain and Ireland* Institute of Cornish Stud Spec Rep, 7

Thomas, A C, 1982, *Christianity in Roman Britain to AD 500*

Wainwright, F T, 1953, 'Souterrains in Scotland' *Antiq,* 27, 219-32

Wainwright, F T, 1955, 'The Picts and the Problem' in Wainwright, 1-53

ed Wainwright, F T, 1955, *The Problem of the Picts* (reprinted with addenda, 1980)

Wainwright, F T, 1963, *The Souterrains of Southern Pictland*

Warner, R & Meighan, I G, 1981, 'Dating Irish Glass Beads by Chemical Analysis' in *ed* O Corrain, D, *Irish Antiquity: essays and studies presented to Professor M J O'Kelly*

Watkins, T F, 1980a 'Excavation of an Iron Age open settlement at Dalladies, Kincardineshire' *Proc Soc Antiq Scot,* 110, 1978-80, 122-64

Watkins, T F, 1980b 'Excavation of a settlement and souterrain at Newmill, near Bankfoot, Perth' *Proc Soc Antiq Scot,* 110, 1978-80, 165-208

Wedderburn, L M M & Grime, D M, 1975, *A cairn at Garbeg, Drumnadrochit, Inverness*

Whimster, R, 1981, *Burial Practices in Iron Age Britain* Brit Archaeol Rep, 90. 2 vols

Whittington, G, 1975, 'Place-names and the settlement pattern of dark-age Scotland' *Proc Soc Antiq Scot,* 106, 1974-5, 99-110

Whittington, G, 1980, 'Prehistoric Activity and its Effect on the Scottish Landscape' in *eds* Parry, M L and Slater, T R, *The Making of the Scottish Countryside*, 23-44

Wilson, D, 1851, *The Archaeology and Prehistoric Annals of Scotland*

Young, H W, 1890, 'The Ancient Bath at Burghead, with Remarks on its Origin, as Shewn by Existing Baths of the Same Design and Shape' *Proc Soc Antiq Scot*, 24, 1889-90, 147-54

Young, H W, 1891, 'Notice on the Ramparts of Burghead, as revealed by recent Excavations' *Proc Soc Antiq Scot*, 25, 1890-1, 436-47

Young, H W, 1893, 'Notes on further Excavations at Burghead' *Proc Soc Antiq Scot*, 27, 1892-3, 86-91